Sunday Times best-selling author Vernon Coleman has sold over 2 million books in the UK alone. His books have been translated into 23 languages and sell in over 50 countries. His titles include *The Man Who Inherited a Golf Course, The Village Cricket Tour, Deadline, It's Never Too Late* and the Bilbury series of novels.

BILBURY PUDDING

Bilbury Pudding is a collection of stories, reminiscences and anecdotes about life in the village of Bilbury, in North Devon. All the well-loved characters are here: the Doc and his wife Patsy; Thumper Robinson, jack of all trades; Patchy Fogg, antique dealer; Peter Marshall, who runs the village shop and Frank and Gilly at the Duck and Puddle. But there are new faces too. Some of the stories are poignant and some are old-fashioned funny and include many topics, from depressed judges to stowaway cats. And *Bilbury Pudding* includes advice on life from Dr Brownlow, Patchy, Thumper and the Doc.

Books by Vernon Coleman
Published by The House of Ulverscroft:

THE BILBURY CHRONICLES
BILBURY GRANGE
THE BILBURY REVELS
DEADLINE
BILBURY COUNTRY
IT'S NEVER TOO LATE
THE MAN WHO INHERITED
A GOLF COURSE
THE VILLAGE CRICKET TOUR
BILBURY PIE
AROUND THE WICKET
TOO MANY CLUBS AND
NOT ENOUGH BALLS
CAT TALES

VERNON COLEMAN

BILBURY PUDDING

Complete and Unabridged

ULVERSCROFT
Leicester

First published in Great Britain in 2009 by
Chilton Designs
Barnstable

First Large Print Edition
published 2010
by arrangement with
Chilton Designs
Barnstable

British Library CIP Data

Coleman, Vernon.
  Bilbury pudding.
  1. Bilbury (England: Imaginary place)- -Fiction.
  2. Villages- -England- -North Devon- -Fiction.
  3. North Devon (England)- -Social life and customs- -
  Fiction. 4. Large type books.
  I. Title
  823.9'14–dc22

  ISBN 978–1–44480–132–3

Published by
F. A. Thorpe (Publishing)
Anstey, Leicestershire

Set by Words & Graphics Ltd.
Anstey, Leicestershire
Printed and bound in Great Britain by
T. J. International Ltd., Padstow, Cornwall

This book is printed on acid-free paper

Dedication

To Donna Antoinette, who bakes the best cakes and pastries in Bilbury (her buns are, quite rightly, widely revered) and whose music soothes my soul.

> If God were kind and said to me
> Go dream a wife
> Your choice is free
> She is the one who it would be.

Contents

The Judge

Most of the patients I saw at my surgery in the North Devon village of Bilbury were locals; villagers whose families had lived in Bilbury longer than they, or anyone else, could remember. Thanks to Miss Johnson, my receptionist, I always had their medical records in front of me when they came in to see me though in many cases, of course, the official records were quite unnecessary. I knew their lumps and bumps and medical idiosyncrasies almost as well as they did.

There were, of course, occasional exceptions: visitors, known officially as 'temporary residents', who did not live in the village; for whom I held no medical records and about whom I knew nothing.

'There's a gentleman to see you who is new to the village,' whispered Miss Johnson at the end of one Saturday morning surgery. Miss Johnson is efficient but kind. She is also enormously discrete and very loyal. She is in her fifties, tall, slim and white haired. She dresses neatly and always has a single row of pearls around her neck. 'He's staying for two nights at the Duck and Puddle. I think he's just passing through.' She put the form he'd completed on the blotter on my desk. I glanced down at it. His name, date of birth and home address, and the name and address of the GP with whom he was registered were all written down neatly.

The Duck and Puddle is our village pub, run by Frank and Gilly Parsons. Frank, the landlord, is in his late fifties. He is bald, overweight and a shuffling advertisement for poor health. He suffers from chronic bronchitis, persistent high blood pressure and an overworked and constantly complaining liver. His wife, Gilly, is tiny, lively and in her forties. They have two or three bedrooms which they let out occasionally to travellers and holiday-makers. They don't take couples with children or young men travelling in groups, and Gilly has been known to turn away couples if she thought one or the other might not be with their lawful partner. They don't have a lot of people staying with them but that suits them fine.

I looked at Miss Johnson and raised an eyebrow.

'Sixty four, sixty five next February, gentleman, smart sounding address on his form, possibly a lawyer though I'm guessing, nice Mercedes motor car, bachelor, lives alone, expensive suit, has his shirts professionally laundered, very nice luggage, silver-backed hairbrush, paid Gilly in cash in advance for two nights.'

I couldn't help smiling as Miss Johnson passed on this information, especially the use of the word 'gentleman'. She blushed lightly. 'He's been in the waiting room for fifteen minutes,' she explained. 'I rang Gilly for a little extra information.'

Bilbury is one of those small, off-the-beaten track Devon villages where the locals know each other so well that the arrival of any stranger is a noteworthy event. The North Devon coast is three miles to the north and our nearest big towns include such urban centres as Combe Martin, Lynton and Ilfracombe. Barnstaple, ten miles or so to the west, is our metropolis. It is to Barnstaple that we go when we need the services of solicitors or dentists or when we need to purchase exceptional items such as new shoes or carpets.

I glanced down at the form. 'Rushmore. Gerald Albert.' Miss Johnson nodded. 'That's what he told me,' she agreed. 'He told Gilly the same.'

'So if he's here under a pseudonym he's bright enough to stick to his story,' I quipped.

Miss Johnson looked at me, not sure whether or not I was being serious.

'OK,' I said. 'Ask him to come in, please.'

Rushmore, Gerald Albert, looked younger than his age. He wore an expensive light tweed suit, a club tie which I didn't recognise and a silk shirt that had his initials on the pocket. A laundry mark was just visible. His clothes seemed to have been made for someone a couple of sizes larger and so I assumed that he had recently lost weight. His grey hair was a tight mass of curls just above his ears, but thinned quickly into a desert-like scalp at the top of his head. He looked distinguished. I could see why Miss Johnson had called him a 'gentleman'. He looked like the sort of man who is accustomed to having people jump without him having to tell them to do it.

I smiled, greeted him, waved him to a chair and invited him to sit down. He nodded but didn't smile back.

I didn't have to put much effort into making a diagnosis because he told me what was wrong with him.

'I'm depressed,' he said. 'I have difficulty in sleeping, I wake early in the mornings, I have no appetite.'

'How long have you felt like this?'

'Several months. Three months. Four.'

'Can you think of anything that might have triggered it?'

4

He thought for a moment and then shook his head.

'Are you being treated? Drugs? Anything?'

Another shake of the head. 'I haven't spoken to anyone else,' he confessed.

'Not even your GP?'

He shook his head.

'But you've been ill for some months?'

He nodded.

'Is there a reason for your not having talked to your GP?'

'It's difficult.'

'I'm not a psychiatrist,' I pointed out, after a silence.

'Splendid,' he said. 'I've never had much faith in psychiatrists. I would deny I ever said this but it has always seemed to me to be a black art masquerading as a science.'

'What are you doing in Bilbury?'

'Taking a short break.'

'How long are you staying?' I asked, though I already knew the answer.

'Just two nights. Last night and tonight.'

Mr Rushmore was not the usual 'temporary resident'. The visitors who call into my surgery are usually suffering from something sudden and unexpected. A chest infection. A urinary infection. Earache. Fishing hook caught in a finger. Sprained ankle. I treat them, give them a note to pass on to their own GP, send them on their way and never see them again.

'Have you been resting? Off work?'

He shook his head.

'Might it not be a good idea to take a break?'

'It's difficult,' he said.

'What about taking next week off work?' I asked.

'I can't.'

I asked him why not.

'I have to be in court on Monday,' he answered. 'I need to leave here early on Sunday evening.'

'I'm sorry to hear it,' I said. I wondered what he'd done. 'Would it help if I gave you a note?'

He shook his head sadly. 'I've got to be there,' he said. 'They're expecting me.'

I nodded. 'They're expecting me,' seemed a sweet way to put it.

There was a silence for a while.

'I'm the judge,' he said.

Suddenly I could see why he had to be in court. And I thought I understood his reluctance to discuss his problem with his own GP. It had never before occurred to me that judges might suffer from the same weaknesses and frailties as other human beings.

'The sort of judge who wears a wig and sends people to prison?'

He nodded. 'People who have done something wrong.'

I drew some circles on my blotter and then turned them into faces. I'd never knowingly treated a judge before. It occurred to me that I might have a responsibility to insist that he signed himself off work. I wondered if I could. Can a doctor's authority exceed that of a judge?

'It's something of a dilemma isn't it?' he asked, seemingly reading my mind.

I agreed that it was. 'How did you come to be here? Why tell me if you won't tell your own GP?'

'I came away to think about things. I decided I needed to talk to someone. It had to be a stranger. Someone who doesn't know where I live or where I work. And it had to be a priest or a doctor.'

'Someone obliged to keep your secret?'

'Precisely.'

'How did you choose Bilbury?'

'I didn't choose Bilbury. I just found myself here.'

'And decided to look for a local doctor?'

He nodded.

'Your name isn't Rushmore, of course?'

He shook his head. 'I'm afraid it isn't.'

7

'And the address you gave on your form is false?'

'I'm afraid it is. Giving a false name and address on a temporary resident form may be morally debatable but it isn't, strictly speaking, illegal.'

I thought about things for a moment.

'Which means,' he said, 'that even if you want to insist that I take time off from work, you cannot.'

'No, I suppose not,' I agreed.

'If it is any consolation I gave a false name and address to liberate you from a potentially uncomfortable dilemma.'

I nodded my understanding.

'But maybe you can help me.'

'Maybe I can. But not in half an hour I'm afraid.'

'Maybe we can sort something out.'

'Do you have a suggestion?'

'I need to talk to someone. If you can find the time. I'll pay you. I can come back. But not as an NHS patient. I'll come to you as a private patient.'

'I don't take private patients.'

'Maybe you would consider an exception?'

'I'll think about it. But if I treat you I may need to prescribe for you.'

'No drugs. I won't take drugs. Drugs might affect me.'

'Affect your judgement?'

A hint of a smile. The first. And a nod.

'Why trust me? You don't know anything about me.'

'I'm quite a good judge of character,' he said. 'It comes with the job.'

'I suppose it does.'

'And I asked around.'

'In the village?'

'I had to ask how to find the local doctor. I pretended to be less capable at following directions than I am. I enquired at the public house and the local shop and spoke to a woman on a bicycle and a man in a small but very dirty truck. Everyone I spoke to seemed to have confidence in your skills as a physician. The man in the truck spoke of you with some affection in his voice.'

I felt a mixture of pride and embarrassment. 'That's good to hear.' I paused. 'The man in the truck was about my age? Well-built and weather-beaten?'

'He was. He looked reliable. Not the sort of man to dissemble.'

'Thumper Robinson,' I said. 'That's his name. I don't think he's ever dissembled in his life.'

'Is Thumper his real name?'

I thought for a moment. 'As far as I know. His family all call him Thumper.'

Thumper is in his twenties. He has an unruly mop of black, curly hair that he is beginning to lose and drives an ancient, powerful four wheel drive truck that has what look like metal farm gates welded to the front and the back. If you ask him what he does for a living he usually smiles and replies: 'Oh, a bit of this and a bit of that.' He is a jack of all trades and a master of most of them.

I looked at my watch. 'I have two urgent visits I must make,' I told him. 'Can you come back later?'

'You choose the time. I have nothing else to do and nowhere else I need to be.'

'Three o'clock this afternoon?'

'That's fine. Does the Duck and Puddle provide a good lunch?'

'Excellent.'

He rose and held out his hand. 'Until three o'clock,' he said.

I shook his hand and, when he'd gone, I sat for several minutes thinking about who he was, what he'd said and how on earth I could possibly help him.

★ ★ ★

The judge was, as I had expected, on time.

Miss Johnson doesn't work on Saturday

10

afternoons and so I escorted him into the surgery myself.

'I suggest that I pay you £50 an hour,' he suggested. 'If you think that too little, please tell me now.'

I looked at him, astonished. 'I don't think I make much more than that in a week!'

He smiled. The second smile of the day. 'So £50 an hour will be acceptable?'

I shook my head. 'We'll find some other way for you to pay me,' I told him.

He frowned.

'Nothing illegal,' I assured him.

He seemed to realise that I was serious and he didn't press the point. But I could tell that my refusal had made him slightly uncomfortable.

And then we talked about his life. I asked him to tell me five things which had made him laugh in the previous six months. I asked him about his hopes, his ambitions and his fears. I asked him what things he enjoyed and what things worried him.

At first he clearly felt uncomfortable talking about such things. He answered vaguely or flippantly. But when I pointed out that I didn't know his real name and didn't know where he lived and that he could therefore treat me as the stranger I was, a medical confessor, he seemed to feel more comfortable about opening his heart.

He couldn't remember anything that had made him laugh. He said his hopes and ambitions and fears were all related to his work. He admitted that his work was his life.

When my wife Patsy knocked on the door to tell me that it was six o'clock, and to ask me if I wanted dinner, both the judge and I were surprised.

'Would you like to stay to dinner?' I asked, as he stood up to leave.

'Oh no, thank you,' he said swiftly. 'I've reserved dinner at the Duck and Puddle.'

Both Patsy and I knew that this was nonsense. No one at the Duck and Puddle has ever reserved a table. But I assumed that the judge felt uncomfortable about staying and that the lie was his escape clause. I guessed that he would suspect that I would know it wasn't true. I didn't press him. Patsy said nothing.

At the door the judge turned. 'I'm not sure why,' he said bluntly. 'But I feel in some way strangely comforted.'

'I'm pleased.'

'I would like to see you again.'

'OK.'

'May I return next weekend?'

'Of course. Are you still here tomorrow? You can come back tomorrow afternoon if you like?'

He thought about this for a while. 'I think that may be too soon,' he said at last. 'I need to think about today's conversation. There are many confusions in my mind. A week's interval would give me chance to clear my thoughts.' He looked at me. 'Besides,' he said, 'I think I've taken up enough of your time for one weekend.'

I started to say something but he held up a hand to stop me. Then he hesitated, clearly wanting to add something else. 'I am aware that you will treat our relationship in confidence.'

'Of course.'

'I appreciate that,' he said. 'And I trust you completely. But, since I may be taking up a large part of your weekends, I think you should explain things to your wife.'

When he'd gone I did as he'd suggested and told Patsy everything he'd told me.

'What do you think of him?' I asked her.

'I don't really know,' Patsy protested. 'I only met him for a moment.'

'Sum him up,' I said. 'First impressions. Two words.'

'Pompous and lonely,' she said immediately.

They would have been the two words I would have used.

★ ★ ★

The judge came to see me every Saturday for five weeks. He stayed at the Duck and Puddle and when he wasn't in my surgery he spent his time walking around the village. He became a regular customer at the village shop where Peter Marshall laid in a good supply of the old-fashioned humbugs he liked to suck as he walked.

The judge and I talked for two to three hours each week. The practice in the village was quiet at the time; I had no one seriously ill to worry about and, therefore, no exceptional demands upon my time.

As I had warned the judge before we had started I had no training in psychiatry and no specific aims in mind when we talked. It seemed to me that if I could learn to understand him a little through listening then maybe he would understand himself a little better too. And, maybe, through understanding would come a solution.

At the end of our second meeting he again raised the question of payment. He took out his wallet, removed a clump of notes and placed them on the desk.

'No thanks,' I told him.

'But I have to pay you,' he said.

'You don't have to pay me,' I said, softly.

'But that's the way the world works,' he said.

'No it isn't,' I said. It was the first time I'd contradicted him and he looked startled. 'Not in Bilbury.'

I thought about telling him that the fee he had to pay would be accepting my time without payment, and understanding and accepting that not everything is a matter of money. But that seemed pompous and I didn't want to fight his pomposity with any of my own.

And then, quite on the spur of the moment, I thought of something.

'Miss Billingham's wall has fallen down,' I told him. 'Actually, it was helped on its way by a delivery lorry which took the corner too sharply. But it has been falling down for years. Thumper says it was falling down when he was a kid.'

'I can't and won't interfere with the courts,' said the judge firmly.

'No, no,' I said. 'I don't want you to. It's simpler than that. Miss Billingham can't afford a new wall and the lorry driver's insurance company will take years before they agree to cough up a penny.'

'You want me to pay for a new wall?' asked the judge, looking surprised.

I shook my head.

'We're going to rebuild her wall tomorrow,' I said.

'We?'

'The village. But I want you to help us.'

'It's Sunday.'

'Yes.'

'I don't know anything about building walls.'

'Nor do I.'

'I'm a judge for heaven's sake.'

'I'm a doctor.'

'You're helping?'

'Of course.'

'Do you know anything about building walls?'

'No. But I can push a wheelbarrow and probably mix cement if someone shows me how to do it.'

'Why don't we just pay someone to do it?'

'Because Miss Billingham would feel obliged to us.'

'And she won't feel obliged if we rebuild her wall?'

'No, of course not. We'll do it as friends. She'll make endless cups of tea and hand out sandwiches and cake.'

The next day the judge and I spent eight hours helping Thumper Robinson, Patchy Fogg, Frank Parsons, Peter Marshall and the rest of the village to rebuild Miss Billingham's wall. Patchy Fogg is a local antique dealer who specialises in selling

16

very nearly genuine antiques. He is invariably unshaven, has a ponytail tied back with a small red ribbon, and usually wears a pair of dirty jeans and a grubby T-shirt. Peter Marshall runs the well-stocked Bilbury shop. He is also the local taxi driver, postman, florist and pessimist. He used to be the local undertaker too until his old hearse broke down while taking a customer to the cemetery in Lynton. Peter has a thin moustache on his upper lip and always wears a badly creased suit and a flat cap. Peter has a reputation for being the meanest man on Exmoor but this is unfair. He is probably the meanest man in England. It was heart warming to see him helping rebuild Miss Billingham's wall. (I later found out that he had been bullied into it by Frank Parsons who had told him that if he didn't help, the cement and sand and other essential ingredients would not be purchased from his shop but from a builders' merchant in Barnstaple.)

At the end of the day I walked back to the Duck and Puddle with the judge.

'Thanks,' I said. 'You did a good day's work.'

'You're a very strange person,' said the judge.

I grinned at him.

'I don't understand this,' said the judge. 'But I feel as though I've actually done something useful with my life today.'

'Good.'

'It's a very disconcerting feeling,' admitted the judge. He thought for a while and then added: 'I'm not sure that I appreciate it.'

I didn't say anything.

'And I'm beginning to get a suspicion that you're not quite as simple as I thought you were.'

★ ★ ★

My initial reading of the judge turned out to be accurate. He was a very lonely man and he perhaps took himself (and his undeniably awesome responsibilities) a little too seriously.

'It's difficult not to take my responsibilities seriously,' he told me when I tentatively made this latter point. 'I have the duty to protect society and the right to deprive a man of his freedom.'

'It is,' I agreed, 'a huge responsibility. But lots of people in our society have huge responsibilities.'

He had shaken his head at this.

'You don't agree?'

'No, I don't,' he said firmly. 'The

18

responsibilities on a judge's shoulders are quite exceptional.'

'If you make a mistake then an innocent man could be locked up for years?'

'Precisely. I don't think many men have to carry that sort of responsibility.'

'Oh, they do,' I insisted. 'They don't bury your mistakes do they?'

He looked puzzled.

'If you make a mistake and send an innocent man to prison there is a chance that he, his friends or his lawyer will fight hard and reverse your decision?'

He nodded.

'What about the surgeon?' I said. 'If he makes a mistake his patient may die. And then there is nothing he, his friends or his lawyer can do to bring the patient back to life. The error is irreversible.'

He said nothing but stared hard at a photograph of Bilbury village green which I'd had framed and which hung on the wall in my surgery. The photograph had been taken in summer and there was a cricket match in progress.

'Even the ordinary GP carries huge responsibilities,' I pointed out. 'If I make a mistake writing out a prescription I may give a patient the wrong drug — or the wrong dosage of the right drug. The result could easily be fatal.'

'Doctors are perhaps a rather special case,' murmured the judge.

'And then there's airline pilots,' I said. 'One mistake at 10,000 feet and a whole plane load of people could be dead.'

'Possible,' mumbled the judge.

'Bus drivers,' I said. 'A moment's inattentiveness could result in a bus crashing into a wall and killing dozens of people.'

The judge cleared his throat. 'These are all exceptional circumstances.'

'No, they're not,' I insisted. 'And that, surely, is the point. Thousands of people have hugely responsible jobs. Most of them have far less time to make their decisions than you do. You can take as much time as you like before sentencing a man. You have time to consider and to reflect. Many people don't have the luxury of time. Many people are constantly being pushed hard, constantly forced to make important life or death decisions every minute of their lives, constantly forced to accept huge responsibilities. Many people with much greater responsibilities are far less well-paid and less well regarded by society than you are.'

Suddenly, the judge pushed back his chair, stood up and walked out of the room.

I waited five minutes in case he returned. He didn't.

I spent the afternoon helping Patsy and our gardener, Mr Parfitt, clear the weed from our lake.

★ ★ ★

I didn't see or hear from the judge for a week. But the following Saturday he returned. For a moment or two I couldn't put my finger on precisely why, but he looked different.

'I owe you an apology,' he said.

'There's no . . . ' I started to say.

He held up a hand to stop me. 'Please let me do this,' he said. 'I can't remember when I last apologised to anyone for anything. This may be the first time in my life that I have apologised and truly meant it. I owe you an apology for my rudeness. You have been kind and considerate and I behaved like a boor by walking out of your surgery.'

'Apology accepted,' I said. 'And all forgotten.'

'I also want to say that you were right,' he said. He paused, as though trying to decide what to say next. 'I was wrong,' he said at last and I realised that it wasn't the words he was searching for but the will to say them. It was only then that I realised why he looked different. He looked calmer and more at peace with himself. His eyes looked alert, when before they had looked haunted. When I'd seen him before he had, I suddenly realised, had the eyes of a wounded and cornered wild animal. I'd seen precisely the same look in the eyes of animals I'd found wounded by the roadside; a mixture of fear, uncertainty and defiance. With rage in there too.

'I haven't been to court this week,' the judge said. 'I telephoned my clerk and told him that I was ill. I have a housekeeper, a woman who looks after me. She and her husband live in a flat in my house. Her husband looks after the garden and drives for me occasionally. They're a pleasant couple. Very loyal. I gave them a cheque and told them to go away on holiday. They seemed startled but they went. I lived on sandwiches and soup which I found in the kitchen. Do you know it took me an hour to find the can opener? After two days I lived on toast and soup because the bread had gone stale. After four days I lived on biscuits and soup because the bread had run out.'

I didn't say anything.

'I needed time to think,' he said.

I still didn't speak.

'It was the first time I've not been to work for ten years,' he said.

I nodded and listened.

'I realise why I've been depressed,' he said. There was a long pause. He cleared his throat. 'I don't suppose you've got any whisky in here?'

I don't keep whisky in my consulting room. In fact I'd never drunk whisky in there. And I don't usually drink alcohol before dinner. But I fetched a bottle of malt whisky and two crystal tumblers. I handed the judge the bottle. He poured a large drink and put the bottle back on my desk. He then picked up his glass and took a sip.

'Water?'

He swallowed and then shook his head. 'This is difficult for me to talk about,' he said. 'I don't usually need alcohol for courage.'

I nodded to show that I understood.

'I believe most people look forward to their retirement,' he said. He took a second sip, larger this time. He reached forward, turned the bottle, examined the label and nodded. 'I've been terrified about my impending retirement,' he admitted. 'When I was appointed a judge it was the culmination of my career. It was all I had hoped for. I took my responsibilities to society extremely seriously. I became a workaholic. And my work completely took over my life. I've never had hobbies, interests or friends. But I used to travel a little. And I collected nineteenth century maps. I gave up those things. I tried to become the person I thought I should be. Dedicated to justice.' He swallowed some more whisky.

He didn't speak for a while. I didn't speak either. I remembered Patsy's judgement. 'Pompous and lonely.'

'I was depressed because I was worrying about my retirement.'

I poured myself a drink. It didn't seem right to let him drink alone.

'This sounds pompous but there is no gentle way to put it. I worried about how the judiciary would cope without me.' He examined his glass. It was nearly empty. I pushed the bottle across the desk towards him. He added another inch of whisky to his tumbler. 'And I couldn't see that I could have a life without my work.'

'I understand,' I said.

'This morning, I walked past that wall we built. For the old lady who fed us those wonderful cakes.'

'Miss Billingham.'

He nodded.

'I cried,' he said.

'I'm sorry.'

'No, no,' he said quickly. 'I cried tears of happiness. I really enjoyed that day's work. I wasn't much help but at the end of the day I felt good. I felt that I had contributed something genuinely useful. And I'd managed it without my wig or my robes.'

'Good.'

'Last night I slept right through without waking. I didn't wake until nine o'clock this morning. I had my breakfast at nine forty five. Sausages, bacon, black pudding, eggs, mushrooms, tomatoes, fried bread, toast, marmalade, coffee.'

'Gilly makes a good breakfast.'

The judge smiled and nodded. There was a silence for a while. 'Are there ever any cottages for sale around here?'

'Occasionally.'

'Would you let me know if anything, comes up? I don't much care what it looks like or how old it is. As long as it's within the village.'

'I'll let you know as soon as I hear anything,' I promised.

'I'd use it as a holiday cottage to start with,' he said. 'But it would be somewhere to live when I retire.' He stood up. 'I can't think of anywhere I'd rather live.'

'Bilbury can be rather quiet at times,' I warned him.

He shrugged. 'That's fine,' he said. He took out his wallet and extracted a small piece of cardboard. He handed it to me. It contained his name, address and telephone number. 'My real name,' he explained. I looked at it and put it into my desk drawer.

He stood up and we shook hands.

'Thank you,' he said.

'No need to thank me,' I said. 'I haven't done anything.'

'You did it very skilfully,' he said.

As we left we bumped into Patsy who was bringing some raspberries in from the garden. The three of us talked for a few moments. 'Would you two be my guests for dinner tonight?' he asked. 'At the Duck and Puddle?'

Patsy looked at me. He was, after all, my patient. 'We'd be delighted,' I told him.

'Thank you,' said Patsy. 'That would be lovely.'

'Nice man,' said Patsy when he'd gone. 'He's changed a lot. He seems much more relaxed. Much happier.'

'I think he is,' I agreed.

We had a splendid dinner and Frank told the judge about an empty cottage.

'It's on the edge of Softly's Bottom,' said Frank. 'The estate agents haven't got their hands on it yet. It's pretty derelict but you could do it up nicely.'

The judge turned to me. There was a twinkle in his eye. 'Maybe you know someone who could help me with that?'

'I'll have a word with Thumper Robinson,' I promised him.

Two days after the judge went home a courier arrived at Bilbury Grange with a crate of malt whisky and a charming note. And a month later the judge bought the old cottage near to Softly's Bottom and Thumper started work repairing it.

Puddings Galore

When I first started in medical practice I sometimes tried to cajole or bully my patients into eating and drinking sensibly.

But, after a few months, I became old enough and wise enough to know that there are times when a doctor should hold back on the good advice — however sound or well meant.

By and large, if a patient has reached his or her three score years and ten I now assume that any bad habits he or she might have acquired are probably too well-ingrained to be changed. Besides, it's difficult to tell a fit and very healthy 88-year-old that his dietary habits are going to adversely affect his health and life expectation.

Occasionally, I find patients who have some very unusual habits.

It was just before lunchtime when I called in at the home of Richard Drummond, to check that a wound on his leg was healing properly.

Mr Drummond, who had celebrated his 82nd birthday just a few weeks earlier, had fallen off his mountain bicycle while riding across a stream. (He was compiling a book on fungi, and collecting photographs with which to illustrate it. He used his bicycle to enable him to cover more territory.) He had a badly cut leg which I'd stitched up, and it was time to remove the stitches.

When I got there Mr Drummond was preparing what obviously looked like a complicated meal.

'This will take about five minutes,' I told him. 'Or I can go and check Mrs Butterway's blood pressure and come back in an hour.'

'Oh, five minutes won't hurt anything,' he assured me, pulling up his trouser leg and sitting down on one of his kitchen chairs.

I opened my black bag and set to work.

'Your wound is healing perfectly,' I told him, when the stitches were out. 'Most people your age heal slowly but you heal like a 20-year-old.'

'Good, sensible, living,' he said with a wink.

'What are you having for lunch?' I asked him.

'Spotted dick with custard, treacle tart with custard and rhubarb crumble with ice cream,' he replied without hesitation.

I stared at him.

'I've always liked puddings,' he told me. 'When I reached 70 I told myself that I would eat only what I like. And I like puddings. So I'm going to eat puddings for the rest of my life — except for breakfast of course. I still eat three course meals but all the courses are puddings.'

'What do you have for breakfast?' I asked him, hardly daring to ask.

'Oh, the full English, of course. Every morning. Bacon, sausage, egg, fried bread, black pudding, tomatoes — the usual.'

'You look well enough on it,' I told him. He was about five foot eleven and no more than eleven stone.

'Regular exercise to burn up the calories,' he told me. 'Most old people sit around and get fat.'

He gave me two paper bags before I left. One contained homemade fudge and the other home-made toffee.

'You and your lovely wife must come to dinner one day,' he said. 'Just puddings, of course.'

'I'd love that,' I told him. 'But I think I'd better lose some weight before we accept the invitation.'

The Ashes

When Patsy's paternal grandfather died he left instructions that he was to be cremated and his ashes distributed on the beach at Combe Martin. He was 95 years old.

'There's a problem,' said Patsy's father, after the funeral. We were holding the wake at Bilbury Grange. 'Cecil Roberts, one of the local councillors, has found out. He hated my dad and he says that human ashes can't be spread on the beach. He says it's against the law.' (Since the truth is no longer an effective defence against those of a mean and litigious nature, I thought of changing Cecil Robert's name for this book. But, he has been dead for 20 years so I feel that including his proper name is probably not excessively reckless.)

'Oh, that's awfully unfair!' said Patsy. She was holding a plate full of sausage rolls which had been made by her mother. Her father, knowing the provenance of the sausage rolls, took one, popped it into his mouth and bit off half. It was, to my knowledge, his sixth.

'How could anyone hate your grandfather?' I asked Patsy. 'He was the kindest, sweetest old man I ever knew.'

I'd always been very fond of him. Until a week before his death he'd spent most of his days pottering in his garden, where he grew the greatest variety of lupins I, or anyone else I knew, had ever seen. He toyed with hollyhocks, stocks, larkspur, nasturtiums, sweet williams, delphiniums, pansies and sweet peas but lupins were his true floral love.

He had spent his early years as a school teacher at the local primary school but had retired at the age of 44 when he'd been diagnosed as suffering from a serious heart disorder. He had, therefore, spent a total of 51 years as a pensioner. I'd examined his heart and had never found anything wrong with it. When he died I didn't know what to put on the death certificate. I wanted to put 'old age' but I didn't think the Registrar would accept that so I put 'pneumonia' down as the cause of death. It probably had been a chest infection which had killed him. He'd suddenly become very frail in that last week. Not for nothing do they call pneumonia the old man's friend.

'I know what it is,' said Patsy's father, suddenly. 'Roberts hates my dad because he won the silver cup for the best carrot in 1933.'

Patsy and I looked at him. If he hadn't been so serious, and it hadn't been such a serious subject, I would have thought he was joking.

'Cecil thought it was his big chance,' he explained. 'He'd grown a big carrot. But my dad was a wonderful gardener. He didn't always specialise in lupins. In those days he grew lots of vegetables — including carrots. He had a bigger carrot than Cecil and he won the cup. He always won lots of cups. At least two every year for as long as I can remember.' It was true. The living room in their house was full of trophies. They were in a display cabinet, on the mantelpiece, on the window-sills and on the sideboard. There were more trophies upstairs in the bedrooms.

'That's a long time to bear a grudge.'

'Cecil is like that,' said Patsy's father, helping himself to a seventh sausage roll. 'He lives near the beach and he says that if he sees us going anywhere near it with my dad's ashes he'll call the police and have us all arrested.' He took a bite out of his latest sausage roll.

'Oh, that's just crazy,' I said. 'Why don't I go down there one night and spread his ashes around in the dark.'

'You can't,' said Patsy firmly. 'For one thing, my grandmother wants to be there. We can't possibly take her down onto the beach in the dead of night. She's very doddery. And for another thing, if they catch you and take you to court you could get a criminal record. Then the General Medical Council will get involved and you'll get struck off the medical register.'

I stared at her, knowing that everything she said was true.

'We could formally apply to the council for permission to distribute the ashes,' said Patsy's father.

'That would take months,' said Patsy. 'And if they refuse us permission that will be it.'

'Why don't we do it next Thursday?' I asked.

Patsy and her father looked at me in surprise.

'You've had an idea?' said Patsy.

I nodded. They don't come to me often but this one was a good one. 'How many people will want to be there?'

'You and me, dad, mum, grandma and my sister,' said Patsy.

'Thursday would be fine with me,' said Patsy's father. 'What time?'

'Two o'clock?' I suggested.

'Two o'clock is fine.'

★ ★ ★

The following Thursday, we parked our cars in the small car park close to the beach in

34

Combe Martin. Patsy and I had Patsy's grandmother in our car and Patsy's parents and sister travelled together.

It was a grey, dull day; entirely suitable I suppose for the purpose for which we were gathered. I was relieved. I didn't particularly mind distributing Patsy's grandfather in full sunshine but I didn't want the crowds of children that a sunny day would have brought.

We walked down to the beach, no more than a few minutes gentle walk from the car park.

'Have you brought the ashes?' asked Patsy's father, in a whisper, as we strolled to the beach.

'They're in my handbag,' replied Patsy, also in a whisper.

Her father looked. Patsy was carrying a large, old black handbag. She was carrying it by the handles.

'It seems strange to think of my dad being in there,' said Patsy's father.

There wasn't anything to say to that so no one said anything. We walked onto the beach. Patsy's father and mother each took one of Patsy's grandmother's arms to help make sure that the old lady didn't slip on the pebbles. There must have been a high tide recently for there was seaweed everywhere.

'Let's sit here for a moment,' said Patsy, as we approached a large boulder. Her parents, sister and grandmother half sat and half leant on the boulder. Patsy and I squeezed alongside them. We sat there for a few minutes, looking out to sea.

'He was a grand man,' said Patsy's grandmother softly. 'A grand man.'

We watched the waves breaking on the shore. The tide was coming in but still some distance away. The sea was behaving itself that day; polite, respectful little waves flopping quietly onto the shore with hardly any fuss at all. I squeezed closer to Patsy and then bent down to fasten my shoelace which had come undone.

'Marriage,' said Patsy's grandmother, speaking to her son. 'It's all about love, support, kindness, friendship, loyalty, understanding, generosity and sharing.' She recited this list of virtues slowly, thinking between the words. 'Your father had all those qualities in abundance.'

'He was a good man,' murmured Patsy's father. 'A good man,' he repeated, relishing the adjective by stretching it out. 'A good father and a good husband.'

'He was a very gentle man,' said Patsy, who had, I knew, loved him very much.

'Do you know, we never argued,' said

Patsy's grandmother.

'He was a very kind man,' said Patsy's sister, who hadn't previously spoken all afternoon. She rubbed at her eyes with a small, white handkerchief.

'Most of us are many different people,' said Patsy's grandmother. 'Have you noticed that?'

We all murmured that we had.

'He wasn't. He was the same person with everyone he met. All the time. Never changed.' There was a long pause. No one spoke. We knew she hadn't finished. She was thinking. 'If the world were made up of people like him there would be no need for armies or lawcourts or prisons.'

Patsy's father then said a prayer in memory of his own father.

We all said 'Amen' when he'd finished. The sky was brighter now. There was blue sky up above and the greyness had gone. We sat for a while longer in the strengthening sunshine.

'I think I'm getting a little stiff,' said Patsy's grandmother after a few moments. 'This rock is hard.'

'Let's just walk for a minute or two,' I suggested.

We walked for a minute or two.

'Shall we go back to Bilbury Grange now?' suggested Patsy eventually. 'I'll make us all some tea. I've baked a fruit cake.'

'Your grandfather liked fruit cake,' said her grandmother.

'I know,' said Patsy quietly. I knew, but did not say, that Patsy had made the cake in his memory.

We walked slowly back to the car. Patsy's parents still one on each side of her grandmother. Patsy, her sister and I followed them.

As we were getting into our cars Patsy's father suddenly stopped and turned.

'We haven't done it!'

'Haven't done what?' asked Patsy.

'You know,' said Patsy's father, lowering his voice. 'We haven't done it. We haven't done what we came for. We haven't distributed the . . . ' his voice trailed off.

'You mean grandfather's ashes?' asked Patsy.

Her father nodded.

'Grandfather is on the beach,' she said.

He looked at her. She opened her handbag so that he could see inside. It was empty.

'I never saw you do that,' he said, looking puzzled.

'Let's go and have a cup of tea and a piece of cake,' said Patsy softly.

We went home and had tea and huge slices of an excellent fruitcake.

'How did it happen?' Patsy's father asked me.

I took my penknife out of my pocket. 'When we were sitting on the rock I bent down to tie my shoe lace,' I told him. 'While I was tying my shoelace I cut a long slit in the bottom of Patsy's handbag. It was an old one made of thin leather. It cut easily.'

Patsy's father looked at me, slowly understanding. 'And then when we walked about on the beach . . .'

'As we walked about the ashes dribbled out of Patsy's handbag,' I explained.

'So he's on the beach now.'

'Your father is where he wanted to be.'

'That's nice,' he said.

'Would you like another slice of fruit cake?' asked Patsy.

Arbuthnot's Tower

Although Patsy came from a farming family her father had never kept hens. 'Never bothered with hens. Damned squawking nuisance,' said her father, Mr Kennett, when I had asked him why our hens were constantly pecking at one another. 'Know nothing about them. We buy our eggs from Peter Marshall.'

Patsy and I kept hens and they were as well looked after as any in Devon. They had all the natural light and fresh air they needed. They had room to flap their wings and chase flies. They could scratch about in the soil looking for worms. In hot weather they could bathe in the dust. They had room for a bit of privacy. And the cockerels lived with them.

Our hens were certainly good layers and they produced plenty of eggs for Patsy and I and everyone we knew who didn't keep hens. Peter Marshall was a little miffed for a while when Patsy's mother stopped getting her eggs from him. But we solved that diplomatic problem by selling him our extra eggs.

But all was not well.

'Our hens are a real worry,' I told my

receptionist Miss Johnson at the end of one morning surgery. 'They keep pecking at one another. They're beginning to look distinctly down at heel.'

'I thought it was just husbands who were hen pecked.'

'Very clever. Do you know anything about hens?'

'Only that they lay eggs,' she said.

'I was looking for something rather deeper than that,' I replied.

'Some lay white eggs and some lay brown eggs,' she said. 'I don't know why. They just do.'

'You're no good at all,' I told her.

'Not if you're paying me for poultry advice,' she agreed. I read the mail she had opened, dictated half a dozen letters and wrote out a few prescriptions. 'Any requests for home visits?'

She shook her head.

'I think I'll just go and check on our hens once more,' I said.

I stood up and moved towards the door but before I got there the telephone rang. Miss Johnson answered and then called me back. 'It's Thumper Robinson,' she said. 'He says it could be urgent.'

I took the telephone from her.

'Could you pop in and take a look at

Arbuthnot Cuthbertson?' asked Thumper. 'He's flying his flag upside down.'

I said I'd go there straight away.

When I was at medical school I thought I knew a number of eccentrics.

There was the student who always wore grey spats and a matching cravat with a pearl pin in it. And the anatomy lecturer who always wore odd socks (one fluorescent pink and one lime green) and who told anyone who noticed (and was foolish enough to comment) that he had another pair just like them at home. And there was a student who drove a twenty-year-old hearse which he had painted bright pink. Outside the hospital he always wore a black frock coat and a top hat.

But I slowly learned that these weren't real eccentrics. They were attention seekers who were playing at eccentricity. I met quite a number of real eccentrics in Bilbury; people who cared not a jot for convention but who lived their lives the way they wanted to lead them.

Arbuthnot Cuthbertson was one of them.

The second son of a rich landowner with extensive estates in the English midlands, Arbuthnot had been an explorer, a mountaineer and a racing driver. He had climbed the north face of the Eiger (wearing a pair of green corduroy trousers, a sports jacket with leather elbow patches and a small trilby). In his twenties he had driven Bentleys and had been one of the famous group known as the Bentley Boys. He had played cricket for Oxford and had missed the Varsity Match two years running due to injuries sustained during his other adventures.

For the last twenty years he had lived in a curious stone tower which stood on the top of a hill just south of Bilbury. Built as a folly by a rich North Devon landowner, who had wanted to find employment for out of work local masons, the tower had been crumbling for years. No one knew or cared who owned it and when Arbuthnot moved into it he was the first person for a long time to go inside. The tower stood in the middle of a two and a half acre plot of land which had long ago been overrun by an impenetrable mass of brambles. Even local children had given up trying to reach the tower.

Using nothing more than a simple, old-fashioned machete, Arbuthnot had carved a path through the brambles and had settled in the tower in the early 1950s. But, instead of simply carving a direct path through the brambles, he had created a maze which meant that the tower was still almost impossible to reach unless Arbuthnot, stand-ing on the battlements of his tower, was

43

prepared to shout down advice and directions.

In the late 1960s, a couple of years before I had arrived in Bilbury, a team of social workers from Barnstaple had tried to have Arbuthnot moved out of the tower and into some sort of statutory accommodation. Arbuthnot had fought them and with the help of my predecessor, Dr Brownlow, had established that the fact that he had lived for so long in the tower meant that he could claim ownership of it. As a landowner, and owner of his own property, Arbuthnot had become immune to the threats of the social workers. When he became a property owner Arbuthnot was transformed from a sad, old man incapable of looking after himself into an eccentric.

The tower had seven doors and 12 windows and, originally, there had been 136 steps up to the battlements. Only one of the doors had ever been operational (the others were there only to make the folly look more beguiling) and some of the steps had crumbled away, making the ascent to the top of the tower a dangerous business. It was, however, up there, with a large parliament of crows for company, that Arbuthnot had made his home. The ground floor of the tower was given over to a large company of hens and several cockerels. They had as free range a life as any hens anywhere and since not even foxes could find their way through the brambles there was no need for Arbuthnot to lock them up at night.

He had made a small shelter from a canvas awning and seemed to live largely on a diet of eggs, rabbits and, in season, blackberries. He never killed any of the hens. He entertained himself with a powerful telescope which, he told me, enabled him to study activities on the Welsh coast quite clearly. I was never quite sure what he meant by the word 'activities' and I didn't like to ask. He made it sound as though he was keeping an eye on Welsh insurgents preparing to march on Cardiff and then Bristol. He was certainly far too much of a gentleman to spend time staring through the windows at a Welsh housewife who didn't bother to draw her curtains at night.

Arbuthnot didn't have a telephone but he did have a flagpole from which he proudly flew a skull and crossbones flag. If he needed help he flew the flag upside down. The tower was visible from all over the village and enough people knew about the signal for he and I to be confident that, during the hours of daylight at least, I would be there quite quickly if I was needed.

I drove straight round to see him. As Thumper had said the flag on the top of the tower was flying upside down but there was no sign of Arbuthnot. Fortunately, however, Arbuthnot had once told me the secret for finding the way through his maze of a path through the brambles. 'Take every second left,' he said. 'And you'll get to the real door at the base of the tower. The only door of the seven that opens.'

I took every second left, reached the door and climbed up the crumbling stone staircase. Arbuthnot was lying on a layer of straw under his canvas awning. He looked terrible.

'Sorry to drag you up here, doctor,' he apologised. 'I've got one devil of a pain in my groin. And a nasty looking lump.'

I unfastened his trousers and found that he had a huge hernia. A piece of bowel had slipped down between weak muscles and had prolapsed. Fortunately, the hernia hadn't strangulated and I managed to push it back to where it should be.

'You can have an operation or wear a truss,' I told him when he was feeling a little better. He was greatly relieved not to have to go into hospital.

'Truss,' he said, without hesitation. 'I've always fancied myself as a truss wearer.'

'I'll get you one,' I promised. 'Meanwhile,

if it starts to poke through again just give it a gentle prod and push it back where it came from.'

'I will, doctor!' he said. 'Damned impertinence.'

'Anything else?' I asked him.

'Since you ask, there is,' he admitted. 'I've gone deaf in my left ear. Can't hear a thing.'

I took my auriscope out of my black bag and had a look.

'Wax,' I said. 'Entirely blocked with wax. When I bring you the truss I'll bring my syringe and sort it out for you.'

'Damned decent of you, doctor,' he said. 'Much obliged. If you'd like some eggs help yourself. There should be quite a few around the place downstairs. Take whatever you need.'

I thanked him and pointed out that we had hens of our own. 'We have plenty of eggs,' I said, thanking him. 'But maybe you can help me. Our hens are constantly pecking at one another. Any idea why they do that?'

'Hens peck at each other to get at the oil at the base of the feathers,' he explained. 'They'll kill one another for oil if they're short of it.'

'So what on earth can we do?' I asked. 'Several of our hens are looking distinctly sorry for themselves.'

47

'Easy,' he replied. 'Put a little cod liver oil in their feed. That will solve your problem.'

And it did too.

We followed his advice to the letter and within a few days the problem disappeared, never to return.

When I went back to take him his new truss and to syringe his ears I took him a traditional Cornish pasty that Patsy had made for him — a large piece of pastry with the savoury course at one end and a pudding at the other. It was a clear, warm day and from the top of the tower you could see for miles and miles. The Bristol Channel was shimmering in the distance and all around us swallows and swifts were swooping and diving. I sat down beside him to get my breath back. The climb up the tower was never easy and my knees had begun to creak.

'Patsy made this for you when I told her was coming up to see you,' I told him, when I'd shown him how to wear the truss and finished syringing his ears. I took the pasty, which was wrapped in a tea towel, out of my black bag. 'Potatoes and carrots at one end and apple and blackberry at the other.'

He took the pasty from me, unwrapped it and looked at it admiringly.

'I'm afraid I can't remember which end is which,' I told him.

'Don't matter a bit,' he replied with a smile. He looked at me thoughtfully. 'You've fitted me with a new truss, cured my deafness and brought me a double ended pasty!' he said, genuinely grateful. There were tears in his eyes. 'Like Christmas,' he whispered. 'Like Christmas.'

'A real pleasure,' I told him.

'I bet you didn't think life would be like this when you started medical school, did you?'

'I never thought it could be so good,' I told him. And it was as true as anything I'd ever said.

A Parrot, A Conker And
A Man With A Cough

Since very few of the Bilbury residents would qualify as 'normal', by the standards applied in much of the rest of England, it should be clear that the qualifying standards required for an individual to be described as 'eccentric' are probably considerably higher than in most areas.

Connolly Ryder had no difficulty in reaching these standards. He would, by anyone's standards and by any benchmark, have qualified as an eccentric in any place and at any time. His dress, demeanour and habits would have marked him out as 'eccentric' in any society.

I first met him when he turned up after surgery one morning and asked me if I would accept the post as Official Grand Senior Inspector of Conkers for Bilbury's annual Conker championships. It was my first summer in Bilbury. I was still very new and wet behind the ears. I knew far less of village ways than I thought I knew. I did, however, have fond memories of playing conkers in the school playground. It was, I think, the only sport at which I had ever achieved anything approaching success.

I had learned that the secret is to strike first and to aim at the conker's weakest point — the edge of the hole made for the string to go through. A sound strike at that point will crack the top of the shell and split the opponent's conker. The second sound strike will push the damaged conker down and complete the split as the conker is pressed against the knot below.

'We can't pay you a proper fee,' he apologised. 'But we'll provide an honorarium.' He turned his head, covered his mouth with his hand and coughed. He didn't mention, and it would not have mattered if he had, that the honorarium would consist of half a bucket of conkers, a packet of 18-inch bootlaces and free entry into the competition.

Connolly was a striking man, well over six feet tall and with shoulders and a girth to match. He was big but somehow, in that strange way some big men have, managed to avoid looking fat. He had ruddy cheeks, decorated with mutton chops, and shoulder length glossy black hair that many a woman would have been proud to own. His clothes were always unusual, to say the least. That day he wore a flared purple jacket, a Chinese silk waistcoat, port red velvet plus fours, black knee length boots and a black fedora which at the time we met he was holding in his hand. He looked like a French musketeer, straight out of the pages of a Dumas novel. He'd been running the Bilbury Conker Championships for longer than anyone I knew could remember.

'When is it?' I asked.

'The last Saturday in September.' He coughed again. This time he winced.

'OK,' I said. September was still two months away. As long as people ask me to do things far enough ahead for me to convince myself that whatever they are asking me to do is so far away that there is no real need to worry about it, I have always tended to accept appointments which are some way ahead without thinking too much about them.

'How long have you had that cough?' I asked him.

He waved a hand, indicating that the cough was of no real significance. 'Just a bit of summer flu,' he said. 'Nothing to worry about.'

'What do I have to do?' I asked. 'Treat anyone who gets rapped on the knuckles with a conker? Attend to spectators wounded by bits of conker flying off?'

I had already been appointed Honorary

Medical Officer to a number of local societies (the Bilbury Cricket Club, the Bilbury Carnival Committee, the Bilbury Amateur Dramatic Society, the Bilbury Folk Dancing Group and the Bilbury Fête Committee to name just a few) and, not unnaturally, assumed that I would be expected to fulfil a similar professional role at the Bilbury Conker Championships.

'Oh, no, no,' said Connolly. 'We aren't bothered about anything like that.' He explained that he didn't want my medical services but that he needed, in his words, 'a gentleman of unimpeachable probity to ensure that the rules and regulations were applied fairly and properly'.

It wasn't until two days later that I discovered that the post the previous year had been held by Thumper Robinson. Thumper is my best friend and I love him dearly but not even I would describe him as a 'gentleman of unimpeachable probity'. Come to think of it I'm pretty sure that neither his long-term partner, Anne Thwaites, nor his mother would describe him in quite those terms either. Not if they were on oath.

'You have to make sure the conkers haven't been tampered with. We don't want competitors baking their conkers for a couple of hours or soaking them overnight in vinegar.

And we don't want players turning up with conkers they've been keeping in a drawer for a year.'

'Do people still do all that?' I asked, astonished.

'Give them half a chance and they will.' He coughed for the third time. It sounded dry and raw.

I remembered a chap I knew at my infant school. He was banned from playing conkers for the whole of the season. Nearly two weeks as I recall. I remembered this because I had recently learned, and not been surprised, that he had managed to fail the modest ethical requirements of the legal profession and get himself struck off the legal equivalent of the medical register. He was I knew serving time for using money which rightly belonged to his clients. He had purchased a flat in Venice and a Ferrari. I mentioned this to Connolly.

'You can never trust anyone who cheats at conkers,' said Connolly firmly. 'A kid who cheats at conkers will always go bad. It's an indisputable fact. School-teachers should keep an eye out for conker-cheats. When they spot one they should have him branded for life.'

'But I'm surprised you have a problem with the villagers in Bilbury,' I said. 'My experience has been that they are pretty trustworthy people.' I paused and thought. 'When dealing with one another anyway,' I added, thinking of the enthusiasm with which one or two villagers were prone to take advantage of insurance companies.

'Oh we don't have trouble with the locals,' said Connolly quickly. 'Our problem is with foreigners.'

'Foreigners?' I said, surprised. 'People come a long way to play?' I hadn't lived in Bilbury long at the time and I had a vision of Americans flying over and bringing with them new types of string and extravagantly tested techniques. I envisaged Chinese peasants riding bicycles halfway round the world to enter the Bilbury Conker Championships.

'People come from all over,' said Connolly.

I nodded and paused, giving him an opportunity to expand.

'We've had people from South Molton, Barnstaple, Lynton, Combe Martin and even Bideford,' he told me proudly. 'Three years ago we even had a chap from Tiverton, though I believe he was staying with relatives in Parracombe at the time.'

I nodded sagely but didn't mention America or China.

'Your job will be to weed out the baked, the soaked and the wrinkled,' said Connolly.

'Not easy,' I admitted.

'Your word is final,' said Connolly. 'No disputes and no second opinions.'

And so I became Official Grand Senior Inspector of Conkers for the Bilbury's Conker Championships. I did not know it at the time but it was a post that I was to hold for many years to come. It was also the position of which I was proudest and the role I always listed on application forms when required to give my occupation.

There is no more archetypically English sport than conkers (the name 'conkers' is derived from the word 'Conquerors') and to be an official, regulating such an arcane sport, would be an honour for any Englishman.

★   ★   ★

Within days I had forgotten about Connolly's invitation. It had been a busy time. Mrs Hunter had her third baby, Geoffrey Parish broke his leg when he fell off his tractor, and seven-year-old David Whitlock got his foot stuck in a milking bucket.

And then I received a telephone call asking me to visit Connolly Ryder at his home. The call came from Mrs Holmes who 'did' for Connolly three times a week.

Connolly lived in a huge, old house on the

eastern border of the village. Once undoubtedly grand it had long ago become rather shabby. The walls were covered with ivy which had crept up onto the roof and was now about to attack the chimney. So much paint had flaked off from the window frames that it was impossible to tell what colour the paint had originally been. The front door, a massive iron-bound piece of oak, had lost its varnish and now stood naked against the elements. Twin stone griffins, one on either side of the door, were now camouflaged green and blue with moss and lichen. When I pushed the brass button set in the stone frame at the right of the door, the bell which rang faintly seemed to be half a mile away.

'He's come over proper poorly, doctor,' whispered Mrs Holmes. She closed her eyes, pursed her lips and shook her head. Mrs Holmes, stout and solid, was in her late sixties. She had a scarf around her head and wore a floral pinafore. She was gloomy and pessimistic and always expected the worst.

'He did have a cough when I last saw him,' I told her. 'But he didn't seem too worried about it.'

'He's had it for a fortnight,' whispered Mrs Holmes. She shook her head sadly. 'Definitely very under the weather. Terrible chills. Off his food. And that's not like Mr Ryder. His bed sheets have been soaked in the mornings.' She always called her employers by their surnames when in their homes. If she'd seen Connolly in the Duck and Puddle she would, of course, have called him Connolly. She leant towards me as though about to share something very secret. 'I changed them again this morning. Top and bottom. Both sheets.' There was no need for the whispering. The house in which Connolly lived was so huge that she could have shouted without any fear of him hearing her.

Upstairs, Connolly Ryder was in bed, though not asleep.

'Good heavens, doctor!' he said, surprised at my arrival. 'Don't tell me that damned silly woman has called you out.'

'She's worried about you,' I told him.

He shook his head, coughed and tried to push himself up the bed but failed miserably. 'Just a bit weak,' he said. The exertion made him cough and sweat.

I examined him carefully and listened to his chest. He clearly had pneumonia.

'Just a bit of a chill, doctor,' he said, dismissively. 'Nothing to worry about.' He coughed. 'Got to be better for the Conker Championships,' he said softly. 'Can't be ill. Can't miss one. Not after thirty years.'

'Is there anyone who can come and stay

with you for a few days?' I asked him. 'You've got pneumonia. You need looking after.'

He shook his head.

'If there isn't then I'll have to get you into hospital.' It was by no means a threat. Just a statement of fact.

'I don't want to go into hospital. If I have to die I want to die here.' He coughed again. 'I've done lots of things with my life. I want to die in dignity. At home.'

'You're not going to die!' I told him, with more certainty than I felt.

'I don't want to go into hospital,' he repeated.

I said nothing, but waited. He looked at me and thought for a moment. 'I've got a sister in Lynmouth,' he said. 'She'll come.'

I telephoned Connolly's sister. She tutted and sighed but said she'd come and stay for a few days. She didn't seem surprised or upset that he was ill. 'I'll ask Mrs Holmes to prepare a room for her,' I told Connolly.

'We're not close,' he told me. 'Never have been.'

'She's coming,' I told him. 'You can't ask more than that.'

I wrote out a prescription. 'I'll ask Mrs Holmes to get this for you.'

Connolly nodded.

I told him that I'd be back to see him the following day.

Four days later Connolly was worse than ever.

'He's deteriorating, doctor,' his sister told me, unnecessarily.

I nodded. I knew.

Connolly, opened his eyes and looked up at us. 'I don't want to go into hospital,' he said.

'I think you'll have to,' I told him. 'The antibiotic isn't working.'

It was only when I went back downstairs that I heard the parrot.

I didn't know it was a parrot when I heard it. I didn't have the faintest idea what it was.

'What on earth . . . ?' I asked Mrs Holmes.

'That's Lucifer,' said Mrs Holmes. She explained that Lucifer was Connolly's pet parrot. She led the way down a long, dark corridor and then opened a door that led into a huge conservatory. Massive ferns and a vine reached right up to the glass roof, at least twenty feet above us. A multicoloured parrot swooped down and landed on a branch near to us.

I looked at the parrot and suddenly I knew.

'Has the parrot been under the weather?' I asked, quietly.

'Terribly,' said Mrs Holmes. 'Mr Ryder was very worried about him.'

'Is there just the one bird?'

'Just the one parrot,' said Mrs Holmes. 'But he goes out and flies with the pigeons.'

I looked at her, inquiringly, wanting more.

'Mr Ryder let's him go out and fly once a day,' said Mrs Holmes. 'He tends to fly with the pigeons.'

And then I was certain.

I went back upstairs.

'I'm going to change your prescription,' I told Connolly. I took out my prescription pad, wrote out a prescription for tetracycline and handed it to his sister, who was still in the room.

'Why?' she asked.

'Your brother has psittacosis,' I told her. 'It's an unusual form of pneumonia, caused by a bacterium found in birds. It needs to be treated with tetracycline.'

'Bird fancier's lung,' said Connolly's sister.

I nodded. 'That's the one.'

'Lucifer,' said Connolly's sister.

'Lucifer,' I agreed. 'He flies with the pigeons.'

'He caught it from the pigeons?'

'Probably.'

'Will this antibiotic work?'

'It will if I'm right,' I said. I paused, feeling uncomfortable. 'I didn't know about the parrot until a few moments ago,' I explained.

'How long does he need to take it for?'

'Ten days,' I said. 'But there should be some improvement long before then.'

'I need to be up and about in ten days,' said Connolly. His voice was quiet and feeble. He looked pale and exhausted.

I looked at him, puzzled.

'It's the Bilbury Conker Championship!' he reminded me.

'I'd forgotten,' I confessed.

He looked at me accusingly. 'But you promised!' he said.

'I know,' I said. 'I'll be there.'

'What about Lucifer?' asked his sister.

'I don't know,' I confessed. 'Maybe we can treat him. I don't know.'

'Don't have him put down,' said a quiet voice. I looked down at Connolly. He sounded as exhausted as he looked.

'I'll do my best for him,' I promised.

Downstairs I told Mrs Holmes to keep the parrot in the conservatory. 'Shut the doors and windows,' I told her. 'The parrot is in quarantine until I can speak to a vet.'

When I got back home I telephoned a vet I knew in Barnstaple.

'Oh we can treat the bird,' he said confidently. 'I'll send a nurse over to pick him up. We'll put him in isolation here.'

'Tetracycline?'

'Yes,' he agreed. 'Same drug as humans. But a longer course. We usually give them tetracycline for 45 days. That usually knocks it on the head.'

I told Mrs Holmes to expect a veterinary nurse to pick up Lucifer and drove back home, hoping that I'd got the diagnosis right this time.

★   ★   ★

Within a week Connolly was up and about.

The tetracycline worked and he made an astonishing recovery. He was weakened by the illness, still frail and needing a stick to move about, but coughing less and looking much brighter. He was also eating. His sister went back home, and Mrs Holmes agreed to call in every day to make sure he was OK and to cook him a meal.

And he was there at the Bilbury Conker Championship.

I did my job as Official Grand Senior Inspector Of Conkers, causing a certain amount of controversy when I arbitrarily banned conkers which I thought had been 'prepared' for the event in an illegal way. I entered the competition too, using the biggest and best conker I could find in the half a bucket full of horse-chestnuts with which I had been provided, and getting as far as the second round before I was defeated by an 11-year-old girl from Combe Martin. It was none too soon for me. My knuckles had already taken quite a hammering and it seemed to be a rather more physical sport than I remembered. Maybe my knuckles were tougher when I was eleven.

After several hours of competition the Championship was won by a 65-year-old retired thatcher who had lived in Bilbury all his life, had entered the competition for as long as he could remember and who announced at the prize-giving that this was the proudest day of his life and that he could now die a happy man. Connolly was delighted to have a local victor.

'We kept the foreigners at bay this year!' he said, with a huge grin on his face.

'Congratulations on a splendid tournament!' I told him.

'Will you be our Grand Senior Inspector of Conkers next year?'

I said I would be delighted to be reappointed but that I thought it might remove some potential embarrassment if I didn't enter the competition myself. Connolly agreed with this.

Just under two months later Lucifer returned home and Connolly was once more a happy and thoroughly contented man. In order to avoid any future risk of psittacosis he decided not to allow Lucifer out of doors again. To keep Lucifer content Connolly bought a female parrot as a companion.

Kittens on Prescription

Sophie, one of our two cats, had kittens one May. She had them in a cupboard in my surgery. Heaven knows why she chose that as a maternity ward. It wasn't one of her favourite sleeping places. Indeed, when she disappeared while heavily pregnant it took us several hours to find her. Miss Johnson, my receptionist, had closed the cupboard door, shutting Sophie in, and if I hadn't heard her gentle miaowing I hate to think what might have happened.

There were five kittens, all absolutely adorable of course, and Patsy and I knew that we couldn't possibly accommodate five additional cats.

'Who on earth can we give them to?' asked Patsy, a few weeks later. We had tried all our friends and relatives and it seemed that everyone we knew already had a full complement of cats.

And then, one day, while I was doing an evening surgery, I had a brainwave.

The patient in the chair on the other side of my desk was a widow in her late fifties called Mrs Bridge. Her husband, rather older than her, had died of a heart attack two years earlier. He'd been very overweight and had made the mistake of racing around his vegetable patch trying to chase rabbits away from his developing lettuces.

'My life has lost all meaning since Albert's been gone,' said Mrs Bridge. 'I've always been a very loving person and although I still feel as though I've got a lot of love left I've got no one to give it to.'

'No family?' I asked.

'A nephew in Durham,' she said. 'I haven't seen him since he was twelve. He's forty-two now. I didn't speak to his parents, my sister and her husband, for over twenty years. They're long gone now.'

'And you don't want to get in touch?'

'I sent him a Christmas card for years,' said Mrs Bridge. 'But I never got one back so I gave up. Didn't seem any point.'

'No,' I said. 'How about joining a club?'

'What sort of club?'

'The sort that goes on outings and has whist drives.'

She laughed. 'I can't think of anything worse,' she said. 'I don't want to meet any more people. I've known enough people. I don't need to know any more.'

'I thought maybe you might find someone special,' I suggested.

She laughed again. 'No thank you, doctor,' she said. She thought for a while. 'Maybe I'll take up a hobby. Something solitary that I can get really keen about. Brass rubbing or needlework. No, not needlework — my eyes aren't good enough.'

She sat and thought for a while. So did I. 'Have you thought about a kitten?' I asked her at last.

'A kitten?' she said, as though puzzled.

'A small cat,' I said.

'I know what a kitten is.'

I got up and walked over to the cupboard where the kittens still spent much of their time. The door was now lodged permanently open. I looked inside. There was one kitten there. An almost entirely white one. It had a brown smudge mark above one eye. I picked up the kitten and took it over to Mrs Bridge.

'It needs a lot of love,' I told her.

'I don't want a cat,' she said.

'It isn't a cat,' I said. 'It's a kitten.'

Almost reluctantly, she reached out and took the kitten from me. The kitten miaowed and reached out and touched her chin with a tiny paw.

'Oh it likes me!' said Mrs Bridge.

'It will soak up all the love you can give it,' I promised her.

Mrs Bridge looked at the kitten. It looked at her.

'What's its name?'

I shrugged. 'It hasn't got a name,' I said. 'We knew we weren't going to keep it and so we deliberately didn't name it. But we know it as Smudge.'

'Because of the smudgy brown mark on its face?'

'Because of the smudgy brown mark on its face,' I confirmed.

'It's a nice name,' she said. 'A perfect name. I'll call it Smudge.'

Over the next four days I prescribed the other four kittens for needy patients.

'Take this kitten,' I told one neurotic patient. 'It will do you more good than all the pills in the world.'

And I still believe I was right.

For weeks afterwards patients of a certain disposition would say, just as they were about to leave the surgery: 'I don't suppose you have any of the medicinal kittens, do you, doctor?'

After that we always knew what to do when Emily or Sophie had kittens.

The Poachers

Poaching was very common in Bilbury in the early 1970s. Some of the locals were pretty much professional poachers. They would sell what they caught to hotels and public houses where the proprietor or landlord wasn't too fussy about the provenance of what he bought. Other locals were just good amateurs. My friend Thumper Robinson was the best poacher I ever saw in action but, later in his life, as a general rule, he only caught creatures for his own dinner table. Knowing that Patsy and I were vegetarian he didn't offer to catch anything for us, though I know he would have done so if we'd asked him to.

Thumper had a lurcher which he used to catch rabbits and hares but he would tickle trout out of the river, using nothing but his own bare hands. Occasionally, he would use a home-made rod and a fly to take a trout or a salmon out of one of the local rivers or lakes. He would do this at dusk but naturally he never bothered to buy a licence. Once or twice he was nearly caught but he was far too fast for the water bailiffs to catch. He had never owned a proper fishing rod. He used to carry a sharp knife with him and cut a rod out of a branch of something suitable. He had a line and a lure tucked away in an old tobacco tin. If he was being chased he would simply hide the tobacco tin under a rock and then, even if he was caught, there would be no evidence to support the bailiff's claim that he had been poaching.

'Who gave anyone the right to sell me a licence to catch wild fish or wild animals?' he would demand.

It was a good question and one to which neither I nor anyone I knew ever tried to provide an answer.

Sitting in the lounge at Bilbury Grange, or the snug at the Duck and Puddle, on wet winter evenings Thumper would often tell me poaching stories. He knew all the tricks.

He knew a country butcher who in the late 1950s still drove around in a horse and cart and who used to catch pheasants using just his whip and one of the small brass weights he used to weigh out the meat he sold. He would tie one of the weights onto the end of his whip and then catch roosting pheasants by flicking the whip up into the air so that the weighted end wrapped itself around the bird's neck.

He told me about a professional poacher he knew who used to catch pheasants by putting bird lime into a cone made out of stout brown paper.

'He would lay a trail of maize right up to the cone, and just inside it, and then wait,' said Thumper. 'Most poaching involves a lot of waiting, and good poachers are very patient men. The bird would follow the trail, eating up the maize as it went, and would then put its head into the paper cone. The pheasant, its head stuck inside the cone, would stand still, unable to see and therefore unable to move, and would wait for the poacher to collect him.'

Thumper claimed he also knew an old poacher from Lynton who had a tumbling dog which used to perform somersaults.

'He'd take the dog out into the fields and the dog would do its tricks,' he told me. 'The rabbits would come out to stare at the dog's strange antics and, fascinated, they would move closer and closer. Eventually, the dog would pounce and catch the plumpest and nearest.'

He said that the same poacher used to catch hares by mesmerism. 'If he saw a hare he would walk slowly in front of her. He would put a stick into the ground and then hang his coat and hat on the stick to make a rough human form. While the hare continued to stare at the scarecrow he would walk away, go round in a big circle, and come up behind the hare. He'd then catch her by the ears as she stared, paralysed into action as she concentrated on the stick, coat and hat.'

Another poacher used to specialise in catching trout with a blow tube, made out of a piece of bamboo, and a pocket full of elderberries. 'He would put a berry into the bamboo and blow it out so that it landed just above the biggest fish he could see. One by one he'd serve the fish a big meal of berries. Eventually, the fish would get intoxicated and drowsy and the man would send his dog into the river to pluck the fish out of the water.'

Not all poachers worked alone.

Thumper told me about a team of six or seven poachers from South Molton who used to enter a wood where pheasant were being reared and walk quietly through the trees in single file. All were carrying shotguns. 'When the last man in the file saw a roosting pheasant up above him he would tap the man in front on the shoulder and then stand still and wait. The remaining men in front of him would carry on their way. When the new last man saw his pheasant up above in the trees he would again tap the man in front on the shoulder. And so it would go on until every man was standing still with a pheasant in his sights. The man at the front of the line, the last one to spot a pheasant, would whistle. And all the poachers would fire a single volley of shot. They would then pick up their fallen pheasants and be gone.'

Apart from Thumper Robinson I only ever met one other poacher in Bilbury. (At least, I only ever knowingly met one other poacher. I had my suspicions on many occasions about how various villagers had sustained their injuries.)

I met him very early one Sunday morning, lying injured on the edge of a riverbank on a private estate just south of Bilbury. And, in a strange way, it was for him a remarkably lucky accident.

I was woken by the sound of banging. I threw open a window directly above our front door to see who was there and what they wanted.

I was more suspicious than I might normally have been because there had recently been two well-publicised burglaries in the nearby village of Lynmouth. A small gang of London thieves had woken up the owners of two large houses, bound and gagged them and then stolen silver, paintings and jewellery worth a considerable sum of money.

My caution was to a large extent unnecessary. Bilbury Grange is a large house but we have no silver and no paintings and I'm afraid I have to admit that I doubt if the resale value of Patsy's entire collection of jewellery would pay for the second class return rail fares from London for a gang of three. But although I knew this I wasn't entirely sure that potential burglars would know it.

So I stayed upstairs and looked out of the window to find out who was banging on the front door and what they wanted.

'My mate has fallen and hurt himself,' said a stranger.

'Who are you, who is your mate, where has he fallen and in what way has he injured himself?' I called down.

'My name is Keith Messenger and it's my brother Christopher who is injured,' said the voice. 'We aren't patients of yours but you're the only doctor around. I called at the Duck and Puddle and someone called Frank told me where to find you.'

'Where do you live?'

'Exeter.'

'What are you doing in Bilbury?'

'We like nature,' said the man. 'Bird watching. Rambling. That sort of thing.'

I turned round and looked at the clock. 'It's ten past five in the morning!'

'We thought it might be nice to see the sun

come up,' replied the man.

His whole story was so feeble that even I knew he was lying. But the story was so bad that I no longer suspected him of being a burglar.

'What's happened?'

'My brother has hurt his leg.'

'Where is he now?'

The man didn't know precisely how to explain where his brother was. 'Over there,' he said, pointing south. 'Just by the river. There's a stone bridge fifty yards away.'

'And a Christmas tree plantation on the other side of the river?'

'Yes!' agreed the man, clearly relieved that I knew the area.

'Give me two minutes,' I told him. 'Wait there and I'll be down in two minutes.'

I got dressed, picked up my black medical bag (which I keep in the bedroom so that it's always ready) and ran down the stairs.

'Did you walk here?' I asked him.

The man nodded.

'We'll take my car,' I told him. 'We can drive to the bridge. It'll be useful to have a car nearby if we need to move your brother.'

'Thanks, doctor,' said the man, climbing into the passenger seat of my car. 'Don't you lock this?' he asked, suddenly realising that I hadn't unlocked the car.

I shook my head.

'You should keep it locked,' said the man, sternly.

I started the car, and looked at him.

'There are a lot of burglars around,' he added, in explanation.

'I suppose so,' I agreed. 'But they'd have to be pretty desperate to steal this old thing.'

He looked around at the battered upholstery. 'I suppose you're right,' he said.

I drove out of the driveway and headed towards the bridge.

'You doctors have to abide by confidentiality rules, don't you?' said Mr Messenger.

'We do,' I confirmed.

'It's just that we wouldn't want you telling the police,' he said.

'I have to report gunshot wounds,' I said.

'Oh no,' he said quickly. 'Nothing like that.'

I wondered what it was like.

Mr Messenger's brother, the other Mr Messenger, was lying on the riverbank. He was soaking wet. His shoulder was dislocated and he was convinced that he had broken his ankle.

'Do I have to go to hospital?' asked the injured man, when I'd finished examining him.

'Can you deal with it?' asked the brother who had fetched me. 'Privately?' He paused.

'We can pay for private treatment,' he added.

'Not straight away,' said the injured man quickly. 'Not now. But we can pay later.'

'I can put your shoulder back if you want me to,' I told him. 'And your ankle isn't broken. It's only sprained.'

The man said he would like me to mend his dislocated shoulder. So I did. The scream would have woken the dead.

'I'll take you back to my surgery and strap up your ankle,' I told him. 'It'll be OK in a day or two. How's the shoulder?'

He rubbed his shoulder and gingerly moved it around. 'Much better, thanks, doc!' he said.

'What happened?' I asked him as his brother and I helped him to my car.

'I slipped on a rock on the river bed,' he told me.

I looked at him and then at his brother.

'You're not going to call the police?'

I shook my head. We helped the injured man into the front passenger seat of my car. His brother got into the back seat.

'We were trying to net salmon,' said the injured man.

'Where's your net?'

He opened his coat and pulled out a piece of white net curtain.

'That's your net?'

He nodded.

'You didn't catch anything?'

'No.'

'You wouldn't,' I said. 'There aren't any salmon in that river.'

'Are you sure?'

'I'm sure.'

'I told you,' said the brother in the front seat.

'There should be salmon in it,' said the other brother. 'It's a river isn't it?'

The brother in the front of the car half turned and looked at the brother in the back. Neither of them said anything else for a while.

'None?' asked the brother in the back of the car at last. 'Are you sure about that?'

'I'm absolutely sure,' I told him.

I drove back to Bilbury Grange, found the man a towel and some dry clothes and then bandaged his injured ankle. The healthy brother went off to fetch their car which they had left a mile and a half away.

'Have you got anything for headaches?' the man asked, when I'd finished wrapping his ankle.

'Did you knock your head as well?' I asked him.

'No,' he said. 'It's just that I get a lot of headaches. Throbbing headaches.'

'Roll up your sleeve,' I told him, reaching for my sphygmomanometer.

He rolled up his sleeve.

'Your blood pressure is high,' I told him. 'It's 160 over 120.'

'Is that bad?'

'It's too high,' I told him. 'You need to go and see your own GP in the morning. Tell him whatever story you like but make sure that he checks your blood pressure.'

When the driver returned I told him to make sure that his brother visited his doctor the next day.

'In some ways it was a lucky fall,' I told him. 'Your brother's blood pressure needs to be controlled.'

'Thanks, doc,' said the healthy brother. He helped his brother into their car. And then he turned to me. 'Do you mind if I ask you one more question, doctor?'

I raised an eyebrow and waited.

'My Dad went bald in his late forties. But I recently found out that he isn't my real Dad. My real Dad has a bald patch but he's not as bald as the man my mother married after he left.'

I looked at him.

'Do you think I'll go bald?'

I stared at him in amazement.

'Every time I wash my hair some of it

leaves home and never returns,' said the man. 'But I haven't got a bald patch yet.'

'If you lose all your hair you'll go bald,' I told him.

'Right, thanks, doctor,' he said. He climbed into his car and then, puzzled, looked at me.

I waved and went back upstairs.

'What time is it?' asked Patsy.

'Six thirty,' I told her. 'Go back to sleep.'

'Patient?'

'Mmm.'

'What did they want?'

'Man worried that he'll go bald if his hair comes out,' I said.

'Ah,' said Patsy, as though it was perfectly normal for me to get out of bed early on a Sunday morning to see a man worried about going bald. She turned over and went back to sleep again.

The Bicycle Doctor

I was brought up in a town, where trees grew neatly in parks and along smart, residential avenues, and where the only flowers grew in neat, regimented rows. Grass was something to be played on and cut. It certainly wasn't there for cows, sheep and horses to eat. It was mown in neat stripes and the cuttings thrown away. It wasn't until I moved to Bilbury that I discovered the joys of living in the country.

Town folk tend to feel sorry for people who live in a part of the world where there are no streetlights, buses or telephone boxes. But to country folk the lives of city and town dwellers seem to be constrained. It is country folk who are more likely to take the time to stand and stare. It isn't that they have less to do, it's just that with the world around you moving at a more reasonable pace there is less of a feeling that life is a series of competitions.

In the country the seasons mean so much more than they mean in the town. Each time of the year brings its own special joys and delights.

Spring brings wild daffodils and primroses

into bloom, turns stark, empty branches into huge green bowers and is marked by the sudden reappearance of animals who had been hibernating and birds who have, like the idle rich, spent the winter abroad.

Summer brings swallows darting back and forth across the fields. It brings bees, caterpillars, butterflies and bushes and trees laden with their developing fruits. It brings untold varieties of wild flowers, ferns and other plants: lesser timothy, adders's tongue fern, enchanters nightshade, meadowsweet, fleabane and, for me the most magical of all, wild orchids.

In the autumn the leaves that have shaped near and far horizons turn from green to gold, russet and cream and then they darken, crispen and fall. Birds and animals, sensing the onset of the darker, colder months, prepare themselves for survival.

And then winter arrives. Skies darken and storms come. Winds break away broken branches and scatter leaves. The remaining animals hide away, tiny becks turn into raging streams and rivers fill to the brim. It is a time that nature cleanses with freezing winds.

Commercial farming, factory life taken to the country, had reached much of England but it had not yet reached Bilbury.

Instead of huge fields full of one crop, the

smaller fields of Bilbury were still divided up by thick hedgerows, and independent farmers still grew what they wanted to grow rather than what they were told to grow by marketing men in smart suits. Walk around Bilbury and you would see fields containing cereals, wheat, rye, potatoes, maize, cabbages, broad beans, peas, haricot beans, artichokes, corn, sugar mangold, pumpkins, carrots, onions, turnips and swede. Not every crop was successful, of course. But, as one farmer had once told me, if he'd chosen a career to make money he'd have become a solicitor or an accountant. He certainly wouldn't have become a farmer.

I learned that in the country it is much safer to mess with a man's car or his wife than it is to mess with his fence, hedge or boundary.

I learned a little about gardening too. I learned that the best way to tell if a plant is a weed or not is simply to pull on it. 'If it comes out of the ground easily and without much resistance then it is a plant and you've probably killed it,' said Mr Parfitt, the gardener at Bilbury Grange. Mr Parfitt looks a bit like a pixie. He has a grey, curly beard and handfuls of curly, grey hair. The pixie look is enhanced by the fact that he always wears a floppy tweed hat, which is at least two sizes too small for him, perched on top of his head. 'The easier it came out the rarer and more valuable it was. If it's a bugger to pull up then it's a weed and you should get it out.'

And I learned that the best way to get rid of moles is to call Morris the Mole Man. (His son is, inevitably, known as Morris Minor). Morris the Mole Man or Morris Minor will fix bottles on sticks all over your lawn and the moles, alarmed by the vibrations caused when the wind blows and moves the bottles, will go and dig their tunnels somewhere else. I learned too that this simple trick only works when Morris the Mole Man (or his son) does it. Try to save his modest fee by doing it yourself and the moles will laugh at you and stay exactly where they are.

When I didn't have urgent calls to do I would make my visits on my bicycle. I did this solely so that I could see more of the countryside in and around Bilbury. There is, in my experience, no better way to get to know an area than to spend some time cycling around it.

My bicycle was an old-fashioned 'sit up and beg' machine which I had purchased for £1 at a Bilbury Church jumble sale. Some of the spokes were missing and the back mudguard had a stay loose and rattled rather a lot but all three gears worked and although the front brakes didn't work (mainly because the brake blocks had worn down so much) the back brakes were almost functional. Because it was a sit up and beg machine I could look around as I pedalled, rather than having to concentrate on a piece of tarmacadam a few yards ahead of me, as is the miserable lot of those who choose to ride racing bicycles. I had originally been attracted to the machine by the fact that it had an old-fashioned wicker basket attached to the handlebars. I could just fit my black medical bag into the basket if I jammed it in sideways. I liked riding around on a bicycle which would have proved perfectly suitable for a prim and proper Victorian governess.

City doctors occasionally expressed surprise that I sometimes did my visits on a bicycle. 'For one thing it's so slow,' said one. 'And for another it's not dignified.'

I didn't much care about whether or not it was dignified (it seemed — and seems — to me that if you have to rely upon your mode of transport for your dignity then you haven't got much) but I did dispute the fact that a car would be quicker. Bilbury isn't a big village and once I got to know the bridle paths and short cuts I could often do my visits more speedily on a bicycle than I could in a car.

And on at least one occasion doing my

visits by bicycle helped save a life. Actually, if you count the life of the dog, as I certainly do, it helped save two lives.

I was pedalling back to Bilbury Grange one day, after completing my morning calls, and riding on the gently curving, slightly uphill stretch of road which heads eastward along the lower reaches of Hillberry Mound, when I heard a whimpering from the bushes on the right side of the road.

I stopped my bicycle, leant it against the hedge and peered into the bushes. Deep inside a tangle of brambles and hawthorn I could see a West Highland terrier. His coat was snagged and he was completely stuck; he couldn't move backwards, forwards or sideways. He looked miserable, tired and frightened and had clearly been there for some time. He had, I suspected, chased a rat or a squirrel into the bushes and in his excitement had himself become the victim; transformed from hunter to potential prey in a matter of seconds. One thing was obvious; unable to move or defend himself he would not last long where he was. He would be dead long before he died of thirst or hunger.

Using the biggest blade on my Swiss Army penknife to cut through the surprisingly thick and woody brambles and hawthorn branches, it took me over three quarters of an hour to get him out. By the time I reached him, and was able to disentangle him from the thorns of the hawthorn and the brambles, my hands and arms were scratched and bleeding and my Harris Tweed sports jacket, which I had previously regarded as darned near indestructible, was snagged and ripped in several places. I had on several occasions released ewes and lambs from such predicaments but I had always been in the car when I'd spotted the problem, and had enjoyed the protection of the thick pair of gardening gloves I kept in the car boot specifically for such occasions. This was the first rescue I'd done without any gloves. Looking down at my scratched and bleeding hands I decided that I would, in future, keep a second spare pair of gardening gloves at the bottom of the basket on the front of my bicycle. Or perhaps, I thought to myself, I would purchase a pair of saddlebags to strap either side of the rear wheel. Then I could also carry a rain cape and a hat in case of bad weather.

I had half expected the little dog to bite or struggle when I eventually got hold of him and dragged him to safety. But he didn't struggle at all. And he certainly didn't bite. He was so relieved to be freed that he licked my face and tried to lick my hands. Since my hands were bleeding I held him firmly to prevent him from doing that.

Many of the dogs in the village I knew by name but I had never seen this little fellow before. He wore a collar, however, and attached to it was one of those small metal tags on which is engraved the dog's name and address.

On one side of the tag the name 'McTavish' was engraved. On the other side the four line address: 'Stein, Primrose Cottage, Bilbury, Devon'. I assumed that I didn't recognise the name at all. I honestly thought I knew the names of all the villagers. But Stein was a new name to me. Worse still, I didn't even know where Primrose Cottage could be found.

It did not, however, take much thought to realise that it could not be far away.

With McTavish in my arms I stood on tip toe, walked a little further along the lane, and examined the countryside in all directions; I was looking for a track or a bridle path which might lead me to a cottage I didn't previously know existed. I left my bicycle where it was. No one would steal it.

It took me twenty minutes to find the track and another fifteen minutes to find Primrose Cottage.

Estate agents would have doubtless described Primrose Cottage as 'delightfully secluded' and 'offering complete privacy' and, on this occasion, they would have been absolutely right. Built in a clearing, with woods all around it, Primrose Cottage had a thatched roof and the walls were covered with a mixture of ivy and climbing roses. The cottage was in a poor state. In several patches the thatch was thin and birds had clearly been helping themselves to nest-building material. The two chimneys both needed pointing and the small garden around the cottage was overgrown and badly needed some care and attention. A small wooden sign attached to the wall to the right of the front door, and now almost overgrown with ivy, told me that I was at the right place: this was Primrose Cottage. McTavish, clearly delighted to be home, started barking and wriggled furiously to be set free.

I stood at the front door, with McTavish at my feet, and looked for the bell or a doorknocker. I could find neither. I tapped on the door with my knuckles. There was no reply. I turned the knob, pushed at the door and called out. There was still no reply. McTavish rushed past me into the cottage. I followed him. The smell, which hit me as I entered, was terrible. Urine and something else. As a GP I had grown accustomed to strange sights and awful smells. I once visited a woman whose husband had died unexpectedly of a heart attack. She was demented and didn't know what to do with the body, so she just left him sitting by the television. It was three weeks before neighbours called me. I find it difficult to remember smells accurately but I was sure that this smell was worse than that had been.

I found the cottage's owner slumped in an easy chair in the living room. At first I thought she was dead. Her head was slumped on her chest. She was wearing a grey dressing gown and her hair, which was grey and looked coarse, hadn't been combed for a long, long time. As I got closer to her I could feel the carpet squelching under my feet. Her feet and legs were swollen. She was wearing carpet slippers and her ankles were so swollen with oedema that they overflowed around the tops of the slippers. There was a huge ulcer in one leg. It seemed to be moving. I looked closer. There were maggots eating away at the flesh. I had never seen anything like it before. It wasn't difficult to see where the smells were coming from. I bent down and reached for her arm. I could actually see the fleas jumping up from her dressing gown as I approached her.

She was alive. I could feel a good pulse.

And then she woke up.

'Who are you?' she demanded. 'What do you want?'

'I found your dog,' I told her. I told her who I was and explained what had happened.

McTavish, who had been waiting patiently, barked once and jumped up onto her lap. 'Damned silly thing,' she said. She rubbed his head affectionately.

'I'm afraid I haven't got dressed or done my hair,' she said. She sighed. 'Not been feeling too good.'

'I think you need to be in hospital,' I told her.

She pushed McTavish off her lap, leant on the arm of her chair and levered herself to her feet. 'I'm not going into any hospital!' she said. 'People who go into those places never come out of them.'

'You need to be in hospital,' I told her firmly.

'No, no, no!' she said firmly. She shook her head. 'I'm just tired,' she said. 'Old age.'

'How old are you?'

'That's a rude question to ask a lady. Didn't your mother teach you any manners?'

'How old are you?'

'Sixty something. Eight I think.'

She was much younger than I had expected. She looked considerably older than

68. We looked at each other for a while.

'What's your name?' I asked her.

'Phyllis Stein,' she replied. 'Miss Stein.'

'Walk into your bedroom Miss Stein, lie down and I'll examine you,' I told her.

'Ah, your mother did teach you something,' she said. 'Never tell a lady to lie down on her bed without asking her name first.'

'I'll examine you and then I'll decide whether or not you need to go into hospital. If you can convince me that you can manage I'll let you stay here and get you some help.' I could not force her to go into hospital, of course. But I doubted if she knew that. I wanted her to walk to her bedroom so that I could see how mobile she was.

'I don't need any help,' she said.

'You do,' I told her quietly. 'You need your ulcer dressing and you need someone to help tidy up your house.'

And then she started to cry.

I asked her to tell me the way to her bedroom, and then I took her arm and helped her there. She undressed and lay down on her bed and then I examined her.

To my relief and delight she wasn't as ill as I had first thought. She had relatively mild congestive cardiac failure, with bad oedema affecting both legs, an ulcer that needed cleaning, a mild prolapse that could be held in place without surgery and urinary incontinence. She was also suffering from an underactive thyroid.

'Can I stay in my home?' she asked when I'd finished and told her what I'd found. For the first time she sounded frightened. McTavish, who had been sitting quietly beside the bed, jumped up onto the bedclothes and licked her hand.

'You need someone to come in every day,' I told her. 'I can send the nurse in but she can just look after your leg. You need someone to help you tidy up. Would you like me to have a word with the social workers in Barnstaple to see if they can help?'

'I don't want any social workers!' she said.

In a way I was relieved by this. I was reluctant to involve the social workers. In my experience they would interfere and hold a lot of meetings but, in the end, do damn all to help. They would be appalled when they saw Miss Stein, and there would be much drawing in of breath and tutting, but I would not rely on them for practical assistance.

'Then you need a cleaner,' I said. 'Someone who can tidy up for you. Someone who can come in every day.'

'It needs a bit more than a tidy up,' she said sadly.

I nodded.

'I have a little money,' she said. 'I can pay.'

'Good,' I said. 'Do you want me to try and find you someone?'

She nodded.

I knew just whom I intended to ask. Gladys Pendle was a retired auxiliary nurse who had worked at the hospital in Barnstaple and lived in Bilbury. For several years she had cycled into Barnstaple every day. But the journey had, at last, become too much for her. A round trip of over twenty miles a day, some of it uphill and all of it along narrow, difficult roads was just too much for her — particularly in the winter months. She had, I knew, toyed with the idea of selling her cottage and moving to Barnstaple but in the end she decided that she could not and would not leave her home. She had, on several occasions, asked me if I could hire her. She had a minute pension, which wasn't enough to enable her to live, and desperately needed nursing work. She would not, I knew, flinch at the problem facing her.

I left Miss Stein and McTavish, collected my bicycle (which was, of course, precisely where I had left it) and rode back to Bilbury Grange where my wife, Patsy, cleaned the scratches I'd received while rescuing McTavish. Some of the scratches were quite deep and needed small dressings. As soon as this was done I telephoned the district nurse and collected a supply of bandages, dressings and drugs. I then drove to Miss Stein's cottage and met the district nurse there.

It took Gladys Pendle just two days to throw out Miss Stein's carpets (all of which had to be burnt), her easy chair (which also went on the bonfire) and various bits of clothing and bedding. It took the nurse and I rather longer to clean and heal Miss Stein's ulcer and to get her myxoedema and congestive cardiac failure under control.

But, in the end, we managed it.

And I was delighted when, almost exactly a year later, I rode my bicycle along the lower reaches of Hillberry Mound, and met Miss Stein and McTavish walking together in the opposite direction. I stopped to say 'hello'.

'McTavish has been stuck in the bushes,' said Miss Stein, showing me her scratched hands and forearms. McTavish looked rather sorry for himself and had clearly been told off. 'He chased something. Didn't see what it was.'

I bent down and pulled a remaining piece of bramble leaf out of his fur.

'There's no need for you to tell him off,' said Miss Stein. 'I've already given him a firm talking to.'

'Oh, I wasn't going to tell him off,' I told

her, remembering the day when he and I had first met. 'And you shouldn't be too hard on him.'

She looked at me, surprised.

'It was the fact that McTavish got stuck in the bushes which saved your life,' I pointed out.

She thought for a moment and then looked down at her dog. 'I hadn't thought of that,' she said thoughtfully. She bent down and rubbed his head. 'Sausages for tea, McTavish?'

From McTavish's reaction it was quite clear that he approved of this suggestion.

The Happiness List

I woke up to find that the car battery was flat and the car wouldn't start. (It was my fault. I'd left the headlights switched on when I'd got out of the car the night before.) Most of the patients who wanted home visits said that they would happily wait until the afternoon when my battery would be recharged. But one, a holidaymaker renting a cottage on the other side of the village who had woken up with a sore throat, insisted that I visit immediately.

It was, inevitably perhaps, raining heavily. Stubbornly refusing to ring my friends Thumper Robinson or Patchy Fogg for help, I set off on my bicycle, with my black medical bag crammed into the basket at the front.

When I arrived, soaked to the skin, I found that the holidaymaker who had demanded my call had made a miraculous recovery and had driven to Ilfracombe with his son to buy some fishing bait. 'He'll be back this afternoon,' his wife told me. 'Perhaps you could come back then?'

I gave her instructions explaining how her husband could get to Bilbury Grange and told her the times of the evening surgery.

On the way back home I hit a pothole. It was still raining heavily and the pothole was full of water and quite invisible. I ended up on my nose in a ditch, badly grazing my leg on my bicycle. My bicycle chain came off and I couldn't get it back on.

When I finally got back home, soaked, covered in oil, bleeding, limping and pushing my useless bicycle, I discovered that the boiler had broken down. We had no hot water so I couldn't have a hot bath.

Wrapped in a thick, soft white towel and with a mug of coffee on the table in front of me I pulled a pencil and a notepad out of the kitchen drawer and wrote out a list of all the things that make me happy. I excluded family, friends and pet animals from the list as being too obvious. When I'd finished I pinned the list to the kitchen mantelpiece so that I could cheer myself up by looking at it whenever I felt glum.

Here is a copy of the list I wrote:

1. Lying in the bath. Not soaping or scrubbing but just lying there soaking.
2. Making plans. Making plans to do something or go somewhere is invariably far more fun (and far less hassle) than

actually doing something or going some-where. There are no traffic jams, airport delays or pompous officials in my daydreams.

3. Enjoying the smell of freshly-baked bread, damp earth, newly-brewed coffee, just-made cakes, freshly-mown grass and tarmacadam that hasn't yet dried.

4. Admiring a tree and working out how to climb it.

5. Sitting in the garden (preferably when I have a great many 'important' things to do) and watching butterflies dancing on air, fluttering by and visiting the flowers that take their fancy.

6. Setting out on a long train journey in a comfortable seat, with a good companion and a book I'm looking forward to reading.

7. Sitting in a café, with a glass of hot wine or a cup of tea and a good book. With some shame I admit that the pleasure is heightened if there is a rainstorm outside and passers-by are hurrying here and there under their umbrellas.

8. Driving home in the early morning after successfully treating a patient who thought (or whose relatives thought) he was about to die.

9. Rediscovering an album of old photographs and reliving the memories they inspire.
10. Walking through crisp and crunchy fallen leaves on an autumn day.
11. Sitting on a riverbank and watching a heron fishing.
12. Walking in the rain in a waterproof coat and a good hat. And knowing that back home there is a log fire, a toasting fork, a plate of crumpets, a dish of butter and a kettle ready to boil.
13. Sitting in front of a log fire on a cold winter's day and knowing that you can pile on as many logs as you like because the log shed is packed to capacity with well-dried logs and kindling.
14. Lighting and tending a garden bonfire on a misty, drizzly autumn day. Having a few rosemary snippings to toss onto the fire.
15. Picking up the fruit of the horse-chestnut tree and removing a still sticky, glossy conker from its spiky outer casing.
16. Taking the first bite of a piece of home-made cake that is fresh from the oven and still warm.
17. Putting the fairy on top of the Christmas tree and then standing back and admiring the decorations.
18. Wrapping presents for a loved one and

then watching them open the gifts afterwards.

19. Coasting down a long hill on a bicycle and knowing that you're heading home and don't have to ride back up the hill (or one like it) when you get to the bottom.

20. Watching newly arrived swallows diving and swooping at the start of summer.

21. Exploring rock pools on the shore and trying to identify the seemingly endless variety of flora and fauna.

22. Building a sandcastle as the tide comes in and struggling to defend the ramparts against the inevitable.

Jingle Bells

Josh Wilkins died early on Sunday morning.

I pedalled over to his house when his neighbour, Elsie Tufnel, telephoned me.

Elsie, who was herself in her eighties, used to pop in every morning to make sure that Josh was 'all right'. (This was her tactful way of saying that she used to pop in to make sure that he hadn't died in the night.)

'He wasn't up and about so I went upstairs,' said Elsie. 'I knew he was gone as soon as I saw him. White as snow and cold as ice.' Elsie wasn't much bothered by death. She had buried her parents, three brothers, two sisters and four husbands before her sixtieth birthday.

Back in the 1970s doctors weren't allowed to put down 'old age' as a cause of death but if anyone ever died of old age it was Josh. He was, quite literally, worn out. In the final year or two of his life he suffered from angina, emphysema, arthritis, deafness, cataracts and prostate trouble. And those were just the diseases that annoyed him because they interfered with his cricket. He had been Chairman of the Parish Council for over 40 years and had been elected cricket club captain in his 84th year.

'I'm glad I'm old,' Josh had once told me. 'At least it means I know I didn't die young.'

He was 89 years old when he died and although he looked every minute of his age he never allowed his frailties to slow him down.

'The best thing about being old is that you don't have to worry about getting old and the best thing about dying is that you don't have to worry about things which might kill you,' he said one evening, a fortnight before he died. 'I've had as good a life as anyone could ever hope for,' he said. 'No complaints.'

'Do you have any special requests?' I asked him when I saw him last. We both knew he hadn't got long.

'For my funeral?'

'Yes.'

'It's not something I've thought of.'

'Do you have any hymns that you would like playing?'

'I don't know any hymns.'

'Well, music then?'

'Jingle Bells. I've always liked Jingle Bells. That's my favourite tune.'

I hesitated. 'I'm not sure they'll play Jingle Bells,' I said.

He looked at me and frowned. 'Then why did you ask me what I'd like?'

'Jingle Bells,' I said firmly. 'I'll make sure they play Jingle Bells.'

'Fine.'

'Do you want to be buried or cremated?'

'Cremated. I don't want to be buried. The worms get you if you're buried. I hate worms. Slimy. And I want my ashes sprinkled on the village cricket pitch.'

'OK,' I nodded. 'I'll have a word with the captain,' I said tactlessly. 'I'm sure he'll agree to that.'

'I am the captain,' said Josh.

'I meant the, er, next captain,' I said softly. The club had, I knew, already arranged for a smooth succession. At a meeting held some weeks earlier it had been decided that the vice-captain, Mr Kennett, would be promoted to captain 'if anything happened to' Josh.

'On a good length,' added Josh ignoring me. 'I've always wanted to see the village team win the North Devon Cup. It would make me very happy to be a part of it.'

In cricketing terms 'a good length' means the point on the wicket where the bowler aims to pitch the ball.

* * *

The day after Josh's death, I called in at the Duck and Puddle as I was cycling back home

105

and saw Patsy's father, Mr Kennett, the new captain of the cricket team. He was watching a cowboy film on Frank's old black and white television set.

'Have you noticed that the goodies and the baddies all have expensive teeth?' asked Mr Kennett. He always noticed people's teeth. He hadn't any of his own since 1949. (Although when Patchy Fogg once said this Mr Kennett instantly responded by taking out his false teeth, holding them up and demanding 'Whose are these then?')

I said I had. A man in a white hat shot three men in black hats. They all fell off their horses, rolled around a little and then lay still. One of them twitched. The man in the white hat twirled his gun around before putting it back in his holster. The television picture then slipped. I slammed the side of the set with my hand. The picture stopped flickering.

'But you can always tell the goody,' said Mr Kennett.

'White hat?'

Mr Kennett shook his head. 'Creases in his shirt,' he said. 'The good guy sometimes wears a white hat, sometimes wears a black hat. But whatever colour hat he wears the good guy always has a nicely ironed shirt with neat creases in it.'

I looked carefully. It wasn't easy to see the

screen but I could tell that he was right. The hero's shirt looked as if it had just come back from the laundry.

'Even when he's spent a week tracking the bad guys across the desert the good guy always has neat creases in his shirt,' said Mr Kennett.

'Except Clint Eastwood in those dollar films,' I said.

Mr Kennett looked at me. 'They're new,' he said. 'Only been out a couple of years. Not proper cowboy films.' He snorted derisively. 'Besides,' he added, 'they're in colour.'

'Did the cricket club have a meeting to discuss whether or not Josh's ashes could be distributed on the pitch?' I asked.

Mr Kennett nodded. 'We had an emergency meeting last night.'

'And what was the result?'

'We decided that in view of Josh's long association with the club it would be perfectly proper for his ashes to be sprinkled on a good length,' said Mr Kennett

'He will be pleased,' I said. 'Or, he would have been.'

I was relieved too. Patsy and I had already decided that if the club didn't agree to Josh's request we would go out in the middle of the night and sprinkle his ashes where he wanted them to lie. This wouldn't have been the first time we had done something like this. We'd spread Patsy's grandfather where he wanted to be. And had once climbed a gate at two in the morning on a warm, moonlit summer night in order to sprinkle the remains of Patsy's Aunt Thelma around the base of a particularly lovely magnolia tree. The tree bloomed in the garden of a cottage in Berrynarbor which Aunt Thelma had once owned. The cottage's new owner, a young London banker who spent no more than six weeks a year in Devon, had responded to our polite request for permission to sprinkle Aunt Thelma around the base of his tree by instructing his solicitor to send us a threatening letter. The solicitor, one of those expensive London varieties with so many partners on board that the top half of the notepaper is taken up with names, had sent us a very nasty letter warning us of the terrible things that would befall us if we dared even to consider entering the banker's property.

Although delighted, I was slightly puzzled by the cricket club's decision. I had once seen Mr Kennett go red with rage when a visiting batsman had allowed ash from his pipe to fall on the wicket.

'That's very generous of the club,' I said.

Mr Kennett looked around, as if to make

108

sure that he wasn't going to be overheard. 'We've got three spin bowlers in the side this year,' he whispered.

And then I understood.

Sprinkling the contents from an urn full of ash onto a good length would, if done at the appropriate moment, give the spinners a huge advantage. When landing on dry ash the ball would get a good deal of grip and turn much more than usual.

'I expect you'll want to sprinkle the ashes at tea time,' I said. 'Between the two innings.'

Mr Kennett nodded. 'As long as we've batted first.'

★   ★   ★

The funeral was on Wednesday. Afterwards we all adjourned to the pub. There was a good turnout. Everyone had been fond of Josh.

'It was a nice day for it,' said Mr Kennett. 'Nice bit of mizzle. Bit of mist. Perfect. You don't want sunshine for a funeral. Disrespectful.'

'Far too warm,' complained Peter. 'I want to be buried in the cold and rain in a damp churchyard so everyone suffers.' He paused. 'I'll be tucked up nice and cosy in my walnut coffin and everyone else will be shivering.' He looked around and smiled. 'Everyone will get nasty colds and die.' Peter's walnut coffin was lying in the store room at the back of the shop. It had brass handles and a brass plate on the lid, waiting for the inscription. He'd bought it cheap when an undertaker in Barnstaple had gone bankrupt. Meanwhile he used it to store tinned food.

We all looked at him. We knew he wasn't joking. Peter didn't joke. He always said he couldn't see the value in it.

'I remember Josh once telling me that he'd been to see the chiropodist and that the man had told him that his feet would have looked good on a man of seventy,' I said, trying to lighten the tone. 'He was in his mid eighties at the time and very proud of his feet.'

'He was a born politician,' said Patchy Fogg. 'He once told me that the secret of political success is not to try and please people but to make sure that you don't annoy anyone by actually making decisions.' He told me that his motto in politics was 'lots of promises but no decisions'.

'He had a great sense of humour,' said Frank. 'It's true that jokes sometimes had to be explained to him in some detail but he nearly always laughed in the end.'

'And he had a good laugh,' said Gilly. 'A fine, throaty laugh.'

'He was a great countryman,' said Thumper. 'And a great gardener.'

'He won the prize for best onions seventeen years in a row,' said Peter Marshall, who had closed his shop for two hours in respect. (He had, however, put a notice on the door telling any potential customers where he could be found.)

'He really loved winning that prize,' said Thumper. 'I remember him coming to see my Dad and telling him that he was getting old and that it would probably be his last year at trying for the cup and that his onions weren't very good that year and that if my Dad could see his way to not competing for the prize he'd be very grateful.'

Frank looked at Thumper. 'Really?'

Thumper nodded.

'He did that with me,' said Frank.

There was a pause.

'Me too,' said Peter.

Several other people nodded in agreement.

'That was at least ten years ago,' said Thumper.

'He came to me seven years ago,' said Harry Burrows. 'He'd heard that I had a particularly good onion crop that year. He was right too. His weren't a patch on mine.'

'But he still got the cup?'

Harry nodded. 'I didn't enter any of my best onions.'

'When he came to me three years ago he said he didn't have anything else to live for except the onion prize,' said Samuel Houghton.

It was generally agreed that this was a pretty clever trick and that Josh deserved to have been such a consistent winner of the cup for best onions. We all drank to him.

'He was very tight with his money,' said Peter.

I should perhaps make it clear that he said this not as a criticism but as a compliment. Parsimony, in Peter's eyes, was a virtue.

'He had a *Racing Post* diary for 1957,' said Patchy. 'He used it for years. He used to write his entries in pencil and rub them all out at the end of the year so that he could write in the next year's appointments. He simply ignored the names of the days printed on each page.'

'I remember that diary. He bought it second hand at a jumble sale,' said Patsy. 'When he got it home he found that someone had ripped out the last week in June and the first week in July. So to get round this he just didn't make any appointments for those two weeks. They were an annual lost period in his life.'

'You're kidding!' said Gilly, with a laugh.

'No, no, it's true!' insisted Patsy.

'It is true,' agreed Peter Marshall. 'The council never met in either of those two weeks.' He paused thoughtfully for a moment. 'I'll miss him,' he said. 'Do you know,' he said, he fetched his paper every morning until last week. He only lived on the other side of the village green but it used to take him all morning. 'He'd set off from home at about eight, arrive at the shop at about ten thirty and get home by one. Some days he would walk back again after lunch to do the rest of his shopping.'

'It's remarkable to think that he was still opening the batting for the cricket team,' said Patchy.

There was a long silence while we all pondered on this remarkable fact.

'He ran out the entire team in a match last season,' said Thumper. 'I think it was a record.'

There was more pondering and drinking.

'He once sued the Devon paper,' said Frank. He looked at me. 'The one you write a column for. Did you know that?'

I said I didn't.

'Oh I remember that,' said Thumper with a laugh. 'The photographer took a picture of Josh's prize bull but the proprietor's wife saw the photo before it went in the paper and insisted that they airbrush out the bull's family jewels. She said a picture showing such things wasn't suitable for a family paper.'

'And Josh sued?' I asked.

'He said it made his bull look like a eunuch,' said Frank.

'That's a cock and bull story if ever I heard one,' said Gilly.

'No, it's not,' said Patchy, as quick as a flash. 'It's a cock and balls story.'

Frank insisted the story was true.

* * *

We talked for a while about funerals in general.

Thumper said at least we all had something good to say about Josh. He said he once went to a funeral of an old aunt of his where the vicar hadn't been able to think of anything at all to say about the deceased. So, instead of spouting the usual meaningless and platitudinous drivel he'd invited the congregation to share their memories of the deceased. He said we could all stand up and say something brief but important to us about her.

'The trouble was,' said Thumper, 'that half the people there couldn't think of anything at all to say about her and the other half couldn't think of anything nice to say about her. Eventually, this old chap who had been a neighbour of hers for thirty-seven years stood up and said that the one thing he remembered about her was that her grass was always cut and her windows always clean.'

We sat in silence for a moment or two. No one said anything but I suspect we all felt that it was a pretty awful way to be remembered. Neatly trimmed grass and clean windows.

Frank said he once went to a funeral in Wolverhampton where the family had the coffin sitting in their living room for a couple of days so that relatives and friends could pop in and say their goodbyes. When the undertakers came to collect the deceased they were invited in to have a drink of sherry with the family. One drink became two and then three and it was nearly an hour later that the cars left the house to go to the church for the service. It was only when they got there that they realised that they'd left the coffin behind, sitting alone on the table in the dining room.

'It had taken them nearly an hour to drive the twenty five miles from the house to the church,' said Frank. 'But the driver of the hearse got to the house and back in forty minutes. Altogether it cost the family an extra £20 for the vicar, who'd been kept waiting, an extra £20 for the grave diggers who had threatened to go home if they weren't given a bonus.'

He said the deceased had always been a poor time keeper and that her family had always joked with her that she'd be late for her own funeral one day.

Mr Kennett said that he once went to a funeral at a crematorium in Lancashire where the staff got two coffins mixed up. He said one of the undertakers later admitted that while mourners had been spouting homilies over what they thought was the corpse of a Methodist Minister they had in fact been paying homage to a Hell's Angel who'd been killed doing 130mph on the bypass. Inevitably, this also meant that a group of leather jacketed Hell's Angels had said a rather noisy goodbye to a Methodist Minister who had once refused to ride his bicycle to the shops because his bell had lost its ting-a-ling.

Thumper said he hated crematoria but that he had once been to one in London which was called 'Dead Centre' and he thought if you had to have a crematorium that was a pretty appropriate name.

Patchy said he'd once gone to a funeral in Chester and that he had hung his best suit up in the back of the car so that it wouldn't be creased. He had, he said, intended to change into it at the house of the widow who had offered to let him use her spare bedroom. Unfortunately, on the way to Chester the bonnet had flown off his car and had smashed into the windscreen.

'It had rained all the way up there,' Patchy said. 'And for twenty miles I got stuck behind a lorry carrying about two hundred bales of straw. The bits of straw blowing off the lorry all came into the car, as did the rain, and by the time I got to Chester my nice, neat, uncreased suit hanging up in the back of the car was soaking wet and was covered with several thousand bits of straw and dust.'

Because he had to drive slowly Patchy didn't have time to drive to the widow's house and had to drive straight to the church.

'I got changed into my suit in the car park,' he said. 'When I got undressed I stood so that I had the car in between me and the people waiting to go into the church. In my haste and general sense of confusion I didn't realise that the building on the other side of me was the local comprehensive school. It was just my luck that the girls' netball team was out in the playground practising. When I finished squeezing into my soaking wet and straw bedecked suit the girls all applauded.'

Patsy said she had once gone to a funeral in an old Morris Minor. 'The fan belt broke,' she said. 'So my Uncle Silas used one of my stockings as a temporary replacement. For months afterwards people complained to my mother that it was very disrespectful of me to turn up at a funeral in bare legs.'

'You should have kept one stocking on,' said Gilly. 'Then they'd have only been able to complain about you having one bare leg.'

All things considered it was unanimously decided that Josh's funeral had gone very well.

★　★　★

There were noisy and lengthy celebrations in the village pub a week later. The Bilbury Cricket Club had, for the first time in its history, won the North Devon Cup.

At the post match celebrations in the Duck and Puddle, Josh Wilkins was declared 'Man of the Match'. It was the first time in living memory that a dead man had been honoured in such a way.

'It was his ashes which made all the difference,' said Seth Pitt, the Bilbury team's leading spinner, who had taken eight wickets for 17 runs.

All Josh's friends agreed that he would have been delighted to have played such a big part in the team's victory.

The Lord Of The Manor

It should have been a quiet summer's day in Bilbury, but we were in the Duck and Puddle having a crisis meeting. The village had been invaded by Americans and we had to do something quickly.

It had all started just three weeks earlier.

A rented Mercedes had roared into the village, scattering gravel, birds and wandering sheep with utter disregard. The driver had raced up onto the village green, already neatly mown in preparation for the next day's cricket match, gone round in a circle and finally parked his car at mid-off.

When the vicar, who happened to be passing on his bicycle, had paused to remonstrate, the driver, a fat man in a pink sweater and tartan trousers, had simply laughed at him.

'There are no signs saying No Parking!' the driver pointed out in a broad Texan accent, proving that his dress sense was in keeping with his nationality. His female companion (whom we later discovered to be his wife) sniggered and applauded this banal but sadly accurate observation. From the waist down

119

and the neck up she was emaciated, rather than slim, and she was festooned with more glitter than a Christmas tree. Gold bracelets, gold necklaces, gold earrings and a gold and diamond watch. Her skinny legs were encased in lime green trousers and her obviously enhanced bosom was doing its best to burst through a gold lamé halter-top. There was too much of him (far more than was expected or required) but, although she looked over-cooked and anorexic, there was also more than enough of her.

From that point on, the American visitors dominated village life and every conversation related to where they were, what they were doing and what they had said.

'They're staying at the Blue Grape in Woody Bay,' reported Patchy Fogg. The Blue Grape was a huge, ten-bedroom house on the cliffs which had, some years before, been converted into a hotel. 'The landlord tells me they're looking for a house to buy in the area.'

'His name is Tyrone Q Yattendon III, and he's bought the Lordship of the Manor in Combe Valley,' reported Patsy's father. 'Now he wants everyone to call him Lord Tyrone.'

Tyrone's wife, called Hortense, told every-one she met that she didn't like her Christian name to be abbreviated, but that they didn't have to call her Lady Hortense unless they wanted to. She complained so much about the cold weather that it was difficult to see why they wanted to live in Bilbury. 'I shiver so much that I can clean my teeth without moving my hand,' she said. 'I wouldn't dare wear a blue bathing costume. People would think I was bathing nude.' Like her husband she was the sort of person who told you how she was when you asked.

When she complained about the heat in the public bar at the Duck and Puddle the landlady, Gilly, trying to be helpful, asked her if she had hot flushes. Mrs Yattendon seemed surprised at this. 'Oh no,' she replied. 'We use cold water like ordinary people.'

They had just finished a European Tour. 'In two weeks you can see pretty much what you want of Europe,' said Tyrone. 'We did Belgium in an afternoon.' He told us that they had stayed at a hotel in Paris where they'd had a suite that had once been occupied by Greta Garbo. He said it was a pity that none of us would be able to afford it. He complained bitterly that so many people in Europe didn't understand English and then arrogantly went on to ask why the English couldn't spell the language properly; why they called an elevator a lift, a hood a bonnet and suspenders a pair of braces.

He annoyed Frank, the landlord at the

Duck and Puddle, by putting ice cubes into twelve-year-old malt whisky. Frank was so upset by this that he subsequently refused to sell the American anything other than the cheapest, blended whisky; he put the bottles of malt away under the counter whenever the American was present.

'I say it like it is,' the American said to Peter Marshall, when complaining loudly about Peter's failure to stock the *Wall Street Journal*. 'You're a disgrace to retailing! I tell people what I think. I'm a blunt speaking man and people can take it or leave it. It's the way I am. I don't like people who mince their words.' Peter then replied by telling the American that he was fat, illiterate and uncultured. He pointed out that the Americans only ever played games that only they bothered to play, so that they could always call themselves world champions. He wanted to know why the American talked so loudly and said so little worth listening to.

The Yattendons inspected a cottage near to Pooter's bridge. When Mrs Yattendon asked to see the downstairs bathroom (and had explained what she meant by this) the owner, Geoffrey Pickles, took her down the garden to a small wooden hut in which a moveable bucket rested underneath a fixed seat. When it was full the bucket had to be emptied into a cesspit fifty yards away.

'There is no lock on the door!' complained Mrs Yattendon.

Geoffrey Pickles looked at her sharply and instantly replied: 'Madam, I have lived here for over 40 years and no one has ever tried to steal the bucket.'

Mr Yattendon, cross about the fact that it was taking two days to obtain a replacement wing mirror for his rented car, asked Henry Waugh, one of the two proprietors of our local garage, if there was a local word for 'mañana'.

'I don't rightly think we have a word which conveys that sense of urgency,' replied Henry.

'They like Bilbury,' said Gilly Parsons, landlady at the Duck and Puddle. 'They want to buy a house in the village. He made his money out of barbed wire and wants to string it up everywhere he can.'

'This village needs dragging into the twentieth century!' the American told Frank Parsons. 'You need more barbed wire, wider roads and more shops. Most of all, you need some big hotels so that more people can enjoy the peace and quiet of your rural English lifestyle.' He announced his intention to apply for planning permission to build a motel on the village green.

'Great central position!' he'd insisted.

'What a waste to leave it as grass and use it just in the summer for your darned silly cricket matches.'

This was not what any of us wanted to hear.

And so, one evening, Frank and Gilly at the Duck and Puddle organised a crisis meeting to discuss what we should do to ensure that the Yattendons did not settle in Bilbury.

It took less than a minute for us to decide on a plan of action.

And by the following evening the Yattendons had left North Devon, firmly telling the landlord at the Blue Grape that they would not be coming back.

It was terribly easy.

We all took the lids off our septic tanks and stirred them up. And the farmers in the village all sprayed their fields with manure.

'What on earth is that terrible smell?' demanded Mrs Yattendon, having stopped Thumper Robinson in a lane near Bilbury Grange.

'Oh that's why Bilbury is known as Pooh Corner,' he told her.

'But the village hasn't smelt like this before!' said the American woman.

'We try to keep it under control,' said Thumper. 'But this is the way the village usually smells.'

And that was that.

That evening we all put the lids back on our septic tanks and celebrated at the Duck and Puddle.

It took three days for the smell to disappear, but it was well worth it.

Montgomery and
Cynthia Hall

In a general practitioner's home the telephone seems to be wired up to much of the rest of the house. Sit down to a meal and the telephone will ring. Make yourself comfortable in front of the television and the telephone will ring just as the opening credits begin to roll. I don't care what people say, I am certain that the bath and the telephone are linked. If you fill the first with hot water and climb into it then the second will ring.

And, if you're a village doctor, you can't escape from the telephone merely by leaving your house. You don't need to tell people where you are. They'll find you quickly enough.

I had called into the Bilbury village pub, the Duck and Puddle, for lunch with Thumper Robinson and Patchy Fogg, when the telephone rang. Frank and Gilly, the landlord and landlady of the Duck and Puddle, were out for the day and had hired a temporary barman called Sidney Weedon.

'You've reached the Duck and Puddle in

Bilbury,' we heard Mr Weedon say. 'And you're speaking to Sidney Weedon.' He always put on a very posh voice when he answered the telephone. He once explained that he did it so that it sounded as though the Duck and Puddle was a five star hotel, but it seemed to us unlikely that anyone ringing somewhere called the Duck and Puddle would be under the impression that they were telephoning a five star hotel. In reality it just sounded as though the bloke answering the phone at the Duck and Puddle was putting on a posh voice.

There was a pause, Sidney put the receiver down on the bar counter, and then I heard the words I always dread when I'm about to eat. 'Is there a doctor in the house?'

I got up, walked over to the bar and held out a hand. Sidney handed me the telephone receiver.

'Just wanted to give you the opportunity to not be here,' he whispered.

'Thank you,' I whispered back. Sidney went through this charade every time he handed me the telephone, even though he knew that I always took calls.

Cynthia Hall was on the other end of the phone. I listened to her for a few moments, told her I would be with her as quickly as I could, and put the telephone back on its rest.

'I'm sorry about this,' I told Sidney. 'Could you keep my beans on toast warm for me?'

Sidney, who was one of the diminishing number of people who regard doctors with a mixture of awe and respect, said that he would.

I hurried back towards Patchy Fogg and Thumper Robinson, with whom I was having lunch. 'Got to pop out,' I said. 'Someone has fallen off his exercise bike.'

'I've always maintained that exercise is very dangerous,' I heard Thumper say as I headed for the door.

'Totally agree with you,' said Patchy. 'Poor old Montgomery. Fancy him falling off his exercise bike.'

I turned back. 'How did you know it was Montgomery Hall?' I demanded.

'Small village,' said Patchy with a grin. 'There are only two exercise bikes in the village.'

'Who's got the other one?' I asked him.

'Me.'

'Not a word to anyone!' I warned him, waving a finger. 'I shouldn't have told you anything.'

'Our lips are sealed,' promised Patchy.

I headed back for the door.

'I'll drink your Guinness for you,' called Thumper. 'It'll go flat if it's left.'

'Thanks,' I called back as I disappeared through the door and down into the car park at the front of the pub.

* * *

Montgomery and Cynthia Hall were relative newcomers to the village. They had arrived in the period when Bilbury had had no general practitioner of its own and I'd only ever met them twice.

On one occasion I had bumped into them at Peter Marshall's shop. They had been buying paint so that they could decorate the outside of their cottage and Peter had, as usual, been trying to sell them a few gallons of the stuff he'd acquired some years earlier from a bankruptcy sale in Bideford.

The paint was a hideous shade of pink and at least half a dozen houses in the village had been painted with it before people started to complain that the village was beginning to look like a set prepared for a pop music video. (In the end things hadn't worked out too badly. A sharp downpour had proved that the paint wasn't terribly suitable for outdoor use and those who had used it on their homes had ended up with exterior walls painted a very slightly pink version of whatever else it was that they had been painted previously.)

I'd met them for a second time during an infamous and rather curious stand-off between two local farmers, Samuel Houghton and Walter Robinson. The two, both driving tractors, had met head on in a narrow lane that led down to the Hall's cottage. Neither farmer would back up (largely, it was believed, because neither of them could reverse very well) and, as a result, the entire lane was blocked for four days. Samuel and Walter both refused to leave their tractors. The police, in the person of Constable Russ Ross, refused to interfere because Walter owned a shotgun which it was well known he kept in his tractor. Constable Ross didn't want to make things worse than they already were. Most locals just drove around the blockage but the Halls didn't have this option because there was no other access to their property. When they started to run out of food I was appointed to negotiate with Samuel and Walter for permission to take them some supplies. This I managed to do. Two days after my mercy mission, the tractor incident ended in farcical circumstances when both men developed rather bad attacks of colic and diarrhoea after eating too many blackberries. They were both taken home in the back of Thumper's van (which had to be washed out afterwards) and he and Peter Marshall quietly returned the two tractors to their respective farms the same evening.

From what I knew of them the Halls were a pleasant and unexceptional middle-aged couple. They had moved to the village after he, a former fireman, had taken early retirement, on a full index-linked pension, after complaining that he was suffering from stress.

With remarkable and commendable optimism the Halls had named their new home 'Dunmoanin'. To discourage unwanted visitors they had put a large 'Beware of the Dog' notice on their gate. The notice carried a picture of an Alsatian which had blood dripping from its jaws. To add extra colour to this stark warning they kept a rubber ball and a real bone on their lawn.

When I'd visited (delivering supplies during the Great Tractor Fiasco) I had found the sign and the evidence quite convincing. I had refused to pass through the gate until Mrs Hall had assured me that there was no dog and that the sign and the fake 'evidence' were there to frighten away intruders.

This time I didn't pause. I jumped out of the car, opened the gate and went into the garden. Mrs Hall must have been watching out for me. She met me on the front doorstep. She was smartly dressed in a powder blue skirt and matching jacket. She wore a crisply ironed white blouse. In any other Bilbury home this would have been unusual attire but Mrs Hall had been dressed quite formally on both the previous occasions when I'd met her.

'I think Montgomery has broken his collar bone,' she said. 'But I need to talk to you before you see him.' She led me into their neat and smartly furnished living room. Large French windows led out onto a small terrace and overlooked a neat garden surrounded by woodland. She straightened a magazine on a small table and sat down on the sofa and pointed to a chair. I sat down. She pulled her skirt down to make sure that it covered her knees, though it already did this.

'Where is your husband?' I asked.

'He's in the garage, where he fell,' she told me. 'But he's sitting and he's fairly comfortable.' She paused, picked up a cushion that sat on the sofa beside her and punched it a little. Then she put it back. 'As comfortable as can be expected.'

I nodded, to indicate that she should go on.

'It's a bit difficult,' she said. She paused and played with her hair. 'Embarrassing is a better word.'

'Tell me,' I told her. 'Nothing you tell me is going to embarrass me or shock me.'

'I couldn't ring an ambulance,' she said. 'I

don't want people talking. Nor does Mont-gomery.'

'OK,' I said. 'Even if you had called an ambulance it probably wouldn't be here for an hour I'm afraid.'

'No,' she said. 'That's one of the disadvantages of living in the country, isn't it?' She checked her earlobes one by one, as though making sure that her earrings hadn't fallen off. They were the clip-on variety and they were both still there. 'Would you like something to drink? A cup of tea? Sherry?' She pulled off one of the earrings and then examined it as though she'd never seen it before.

I held up a hand. 'No thanks.'

She put the earring back into position.

'You're going to have to tell me eventually,' I pointed out. 'And the longer you wait the more difficult you're going to find it will be.'

'Montgomery was on the exercise bicycle,' she said. 'He likes to keep fit.'

I nodded.

'He's very fit for a man of his age.'

'He looks fit,' I agreed. 'At least he did when I last saw him.'

'He's only a couple of pounds overweight.'

'Good.'

'He had a portable television set balanced on a pile of boxes so that he could watch it while he pedalled.'

'Splendid idea.'

'But when he reached out to change channels the bicycle tipped over.'

'Oh dear,' I said, nodding as though this was something that happened all the time.

'The problem is that Montgomery wasn't dressed normally when he fell.'

'I wouldn't imagine he was,' I agreed. 'People wear all sorts of funny things when they're exercising. I once had a pair of hideous, fluorescent-orange running shorts. And a bloke I shared a flat with had a pale blue tracksuit made of something shiny and slightly luminous.'

'Perhaps you'd better come and take a look,' said Mrs Hall standing up. She tugged at the sides of her skirt again.

I followed her out of the living room, through the kitchen, out of the back door and into the garage.

Montgomery was sitting on a plastic garden chair holding his shoulder and keeping very still. The exercise bicycle that had thrown him onto the floor was lying on its side. The television set was still on. Black and white actors dressed as cowboys were shooting black and white actors dressed as Red Indians. It was no surprise at all to see that the men dressed as cowboys seemed to be winning.

Montgomery was wearing a dark blue skirt with a slit up one side, a pale blue blouse, black stockings, a pair of black court shoes, a dark, shoulder length wig and half a pound of make-up. 'You've broken your collar bone,' I told him when I'd examined him. 'You'll need an X-ray and some strapping. There's no real point in doing an X-ray because it's obvious what's wrong. But they'll do one anyway.'

'I'm sorry about you seeing me like this,' he said.

'No need to apologise,' I told him. 'Scottish men wear skirts with great pride. Cross-dressing is revered in Scotland. There are whole regiments of transvestites up there. Why shouldn't you?'

'You're very understanding.'

'Nothing to be understanding about.'

'Would you do something for me, please?'

'Of course.'

'Help me out of my damned corset. It's killing me,' whispered Montgomery.

'I expect it is,' I agreed. 'I take it you would rather change into something less comfortable before you go to hospital?'

Montgomery nodded and smiled weakly.

'Start removing his make-up,' I told Cynthia. 'I'll pop out to the car for some temporary strapping.'

We had to cut through the sleeve of the

blouse and unclip the straps of his corset but we managed to undress Montgomery without too much trouble. It took us nearly thirty minutes for Cynthia to remove all the make up.

'I've been cross-dressing for years,' said Montgomery. 'I can't remember exactly how it started. But I kept it secret from Cynthia for ages.'

'When I first found his underwear hidden at the back of the wardrobe I thought he had another woman,' said Cynthia. 'I thought it was stuff he'd bought for her. And he was so ashamed and embarrassed that he didn't contradict me when I confronted him.'

'You let your wife think you were having an affair rather than let her know that you dressed in feminine clothing?'

Montgomery nodded and winced.

'Just keep as still as you can,' I told him, unfastening a stocking and pulling it down his leg. Cynthia removed the other one.

'I was so relieved when I found that he wasn't having an affair,' said Cynthia. 'I didn't care about the cross-dressing.'

'Now she does my make-up for me,' said Montgomery.

'Very good it was too,' I said.

They both looked pleased.

'Do you think so?' said Montgomery.

'Absolutely,' I said.

It took another ten minutes to get him into a pair of Y-fronts, a pair of trousers and a pair of slip-on shoes and to get his good arm into the sleeve of a baggy old shirt. I bandaged him up so that he wouldn't be too uncomfortable.

When we were finished I offered to drive him to the hospital (explaining that it would be quicker than waiting for an ambulance) but Mrs Hall said that she could do it herself and that there was really no need for me to bother. We were about to get him into the car when Cynthia noticed that his fingernails were still painted scarlet. And when she'd found the nail varnish remover and cleaned them he remembered that his toenails were painted the same colour.

It was half past three by the time I watched Cynthia drive Montgomery off towards Barnstaple. It was far too late to go back to the Duck and Puddle. My beans on toast would be in the bin. But, since I hate waste, I was comforted by the thought that Thumper had doubtless drunk my Guinness.

Cat Up A Tree

There is no fire station or fire engine in Bilbury. On those rare occasions when there is a fire in the village which cannot be dealt with effectively by villagers wielding metal buckets and garden hoses we have to telephone Barnstaple and ask for an engine and crew to be sent out. Since Bilburians are proud of being self-contained this is something we try to do as infrequently as possible. In 1952, a large fire at the vicarage (caused, it is rumoured, when the vicar fell asleep in his study and let his post-prandial cigar slip to the floor and set fire to the carpet) was effectively extinguished by a human chain, twenty galvanised buckets and the contents of the carp pond at the bottom of the vicarage garden.

Only once in the last ten years have we had to call the fire brigade. And on that occasion it wasn't because there was a fire. It was because Mrs Pettigrew's cat (a plump and usually lazy mackerel tabby called Catarina who was, on occasion, surprisingly agile) had got stuck up a large oak tree at the end of her garden.

138

Agatha Pettigrew was a dedicated and committed ailurophile. In her late sixties, she had never been married, never had a job and never lived anywhere other than in Bilbury. She only rarely ventured outside the village boundaries (once a year she went shopping in Barnstaple and that, she said, provided her with more than enough excitement) and once told me that she had never once spent a night away from the cottage where she'd been born and raised. Her parents, both long dead, had left her the cottage and she lived on a small unearned income derived from a modest portfolio of National Savings certificates and an even smaller income derived from the sale of stories about her cats; delicate, loving tales which she illustrated herself with pen and ink line drawings. She supplemented this totally inadequate income by growing much of her own food and mending her clothes until each item contained so many patches and darns that the original colour of the garment was no longer discernible.

Mrs Pettigrew's one luxury was her cats.

Some people scrimp and save in order to buy beer, wine, tobacco or expensive frocks. Others forego more basic delights in order to buy rare stamps or commemorative ashtrays.

Mrs Pettigrew fed herself on home-made leek and potato soup and occasional mutton stew, and at the village shop was a regular buyer of dented tins which had lost their labels and were, therefore, culinary mysteries offered at a heavily discounted price.

Everything Mrs Pettigrew did not have to spend on survival she spent on her three cats: Catarina, Chloe and Chantelle. She bought them the best of everything and gave them all her love.

When I received a message asking me to visit Mrs Pettigrew I was surprised. I knew where she lived, I'd met her once or twice at Peter Marshall's village shop and I'd often seen her tending her vegetables as I'd cycled past her cottage. If I had time I would stop and pass the time of day.

Mrs Pettigrew knew and understood cats better than anyone I'd ever met, and our conversations always turned to feline matters. We might start by talking about the weather, the slug population or the first sighting of the summer's swallow but it would never be too long before we were talking about cats. I didn't mind a bit. I love cats and am always happy to talk about them.

It was Mrs Pettigrew who told me that cats purr not just when they are contented but also when they are injured or in pain.

'Cats purr at a frequency of 25 to 50 hertz,' she had told me, one summer morning when

I'd stopped to admire her runner beans. 'It's the best frequency for bone growth and fracture healing and for the repair of tendons. It's also good for healing muscle and ligament injuries and for strengthening and toning muscles. You doctors could learn a thing or two from cats. Purring helps heal joint injury, it encourages wound healing, reduction of swelling and infection, pain relief and relief of chronic pulmonary disease.'

It was, Mrs Pettigrew told me, because of the purring that cats suffer from fewer diseases than dogs, and heal better and more quickly too.

It was also Mrs Pettigrew who explained to me a couple of things that had puzzled me for ages.

'Why do my cats always want to sit on whatever it is that I'm reading? I've got two cats and if I sit down with a book or newspaper one of them will always plonk themselves down on the bit I happen to be reading at the time.'

Mrs Pettigrew had laughed. 'Cats like attention,' she said. 'If you're giving all your attention to a book then they'll know that is the place to be. By lying on top of the book you're reading they'll get your attention. Simple!'

'And why do they like to lie on my

typewriter keyboard? Sophie in particular loves it.'

'You have to learn to think like a cat if you want to understand cats,' said Mrs Pettigrew. 'Your typewriter keys mould themselves very well to the cat's shape and whenever the cat moves the keys will move with her, adapting to her as she stretches and rolls from side to side.' She'd moved backwards and forwards as she'd explained this to me, as though she were a cat, making herself comfortable on a huge keyboard.

But, well as I knew her, I'd never been called to attend Mrs Pettigrew professionally. And, as I drove to her home I wondered what on earth could have happened to require my services.

'It's Catarina,' Mrs Pettigrew explained. She was clearly quite distressed. She held a handkerchief to her nose and blew hard. It sounded like a foghorn.

'Your cat?'

She nodded.

'I didn't know who else to telephone,' she said, apologetically.

'That's OK,' I assured her. 'What's wrong with her?'

'She's up there,' said Mrs Pettigrew, pointing to the large oak tree at the front of her cottage garden. 'The poor dear's stuck.'

I looked at the tree and could just make out Catarina. She was tucked into a fork two thirds of the way up the tree, almost hidden by the foliage.

'How long has she been up there?'

'Four and three quarter hours,' replied Mrs Pettigrew instantly.

I scratched my head.

'You've tried a saucer of milk?'

'She doesn't like milk,' said Mrs Pettigrew. 'But I've tried salmon, chicken, pilchards and clotted cream.'

'No luck?'

'She wouldn't budge.'

'And you think she's stuck?'

'Definitely,' said Mrs Pettigrew. 'I know her. She's definitely stuck. She won't show it because she's proud, but she's frightened.'

'Do you have a ladder?'

Mrs Pettigrew thought for a moment. 'I've got some steps in the kitchen,' she said. 'I use them to reach the cupboard over the sink.'

'I don't think they'll be high enough. You don't have a ladder?'

She shook her head.

I looked up at Catarina and scratched my head again. 'I'm afraid we'll have to ring the fire brigade,' I told Mrs Pettigrew.

'But we haven't got a fire brigade,' Mrs Pettigrew pointed out. Like many villagers she didn't like to recognise that there was a world outside Bilbury.

'They've got one in Barnstaple,' I pointed out.

'Foreigners!' said Mrs Pettigrew, alarmed. 'That will mean foreigners handling Catarina. She won't like that. Not a bit.' She shivered.

In the end I managed to persuade her that we didn't have much of a choice. And I telephoned the fire brigade.

'Bilbury?' said a voice at the other end of the phone. 'Is Bilbury in Devon?' He called to someone in his office. 'Do we cover Bilbury?' He brightened up when I told him the problem. 'Oh, right,' he said. 'Goody. We haven't had a cat for weeks. The chaps love a stuck cat.' There was a pause. 'Is it urgent?'

'Well, it is sort of urgent,' I replied.

'Splendid,' said the man. 'I'll come on the engine myself. I can ring the bell.'

I put the telephone down and turned to Mrs Pettigrew. 'They're on their way,' I told her.

'Oh you are wonderful!' she said. 'I knew you'd know what to do.'

'Why don't you put the kettle on and make a nice cup of tea?' I asked her. In an emergency the making and drinking of a nice cup of tea are crucial.

She put the kettle on and while we waited for it to boil we sat down at the table and talked about snails, rhododendrons and cats.

'Maybe I'll just go and check on her,' said Mrs Pettigrew getting up from her chair. 'Oh no!' she squealed. 'I don't need to. Here she is!'

I looked down. Catarina was standing there looking up at us.

'Oh my clever little sweet pussycat!' cried Mrs Pettigrew. She scooped up the cat and clutched it to her bosom. The cat purred but made no discernible protest.

'I'd better ring the fire brigade,' I told her, wondering whether there was a penalty for making hoax calls to the fire brigade.

'They're on their way!' a new voice assured me when I'd rung. 'Should be with you in another fifteen minutes. I've just had them on the radio. They got stuck behind a hay cart and had to make a detour via Combe Martin.'

I wanted to tell him the cat was safe but I couldn't bring myself to say the words. While I hesitated the operator broke the connection. I stared at the phone wondering whether or not to call him back.

Just then Thumper Robinson arrived. 'I saw the doc's car here and guessed you'd have the kettle on,' he told Mrs Pettigrew as he burst into her kitchen. 'Have you got any of that wonderful Madeira cake of yours?' Thumper Robinson is my oldest and best friend in Bilbury. He earns his living buying and selling cars and antiques, doing odd jobs and helping people out.

I explained what had happened.

Thumper shook his head and sucked in half a lung full of air.

'Trouble?' I asked him.

'They won't like it,' he said. 'And to be honest it'll give the village a bad name. We'll be a bit of a laughing stock. The local paper will make us look like idiots.'

He and I stared at each other. Mrs Pettigrew was too busy feeding Catarina to care.

'So what do we do?' I asked. 'They'll be here in minutes!'

'We'll put the cat back up the tree,' said Thumper suddenly.

Mrs Pettigrew looked up and started to protest.

'Only for a few minutes,' said Thumper, holding up a hand to silence her. 'No option. When the firemen get to that tree they've got to find a cat up it.'

'Mrs Pettigrew hasn't got a ladder,' I told him. 'And I doubt if there's a ladder in the village big enough.'

'Don't need a ladder to get up there,' insisted Thumper with a smile.

And he didn't.

He put Catarina down his shirt so that he would have both hands free and went up the tree as though he was going up the staircase at home. He deposited the cat in the fork we pointed out and was back down on the ground a minute and a half before the Barnstaple fire engine appeared.

'Do you mind if we wait a moment,' asked the Chief Fireman. 'The photographer from the local paper is following us. He'll be here in a couple of minutes.'

Knowing that Catarina was safe, and had a tummy full of salmon, Mrs Pettigrew said that would be fine with her. And so the fire brigade waited until the photographer arrived and then, when he turned up, the youngest fireman, who'd never had his picture in the paper and who was plucking up courage to ask his girlfriend to marry him, climbed up their turntable ladder and collected Catarina. He then held her up so that the photographer could take a picture that would impress his girlfriend and make sure he got the answer he wanted when he popped the question.

And then Mrs Pettigrew gave everyone except the driver a glass of her home-made

Parsnip wine and made a fresh pot of tea for the driver. Everyone had a slice of her Madeira cake before they went home and told of derring-do and brave adventures out in the wilds of Bilbury village.

The Witch And The Bully

Elsie Fingleton didn't live in Bilbury and, strictly speaking, shouldn't have been a patient of mine at all. She lived in a small, rented, terraced cottage near the beach in Combe Martin and remained on my list of patients because she'd lived in Bilbury for over half a century and wanted to retain as many links with the village as she could. Dr Brownlow, my predecessor and mentor, had saved her life in 1954 when she'd had an attack of asthma which had developed into status asthmaticus. Apart from being an asthma sufferer she was also one of the most nervous people I knew. She once told me that she slept with the light on in her bedroom.

'What are you frightened of?' I had asked her. 'Burglars? Ghosts? Things that go bump in the night?'

'All of those,' she had replied instantly.

She came to see me one day in a terrible state. She was literally shaking from head to toe.

'What on earth is the matter?'

'I'm going to die a horrible death,' she whispered.

149

'Why do you say that?'

'I've been told,' she said.

'Who has told you?'

'Beryl Hardcastle.'

'Who is Beryl Hardcastle?'

'She's a medium,' said Elsie. 'She came to the door and told me.'

'She came to your cottage?'

'Yes. She says her name is Queen Julianna and that she is a Gypsy queen but I was at school with her and her real name is Beryl Hardcastle and her father had a chip shop.'

'She didn't recognise you?'

Elsie shook her head.

'Why do you believe what she says if you know she's lying about who she is?'

Elsie looked at me blankly. 'I don't know,' she said. She looked down at her hands. 'She frightens me.'

'What did she tell you?'

'She said I wasn't to tell anyone.'

'You can tell me. I'm your doctor.'

'Will it be all right?'

'Yes. I promise.'

'She said that I had to talk to the Black Angel every week to stop him killing me.'

'And do you have to give the Black Angel money?'

'Oh no,' said Elsie.

'You just have to talk to him?'

She nodded.

'No money?'

'Only to Beryl. Queen Juliana.'

'You have to give her money?'

'To give her the strength to contact the Black Angel for me. I can't do it without her.'

'How much do you have to give Beryl?'

'£20.'

'£20 every week?'

'Yes. And I can't afford it. I've sold everything I can sell. Now I haven't got any more money. So I can't talk to the Black Angel and he will kill me.'

I tried to explain to Elsie that it was all nonsense. I told her that Beryl was simply tricking her into handing over money. But, although I think she knew that what I was saying was the truth, Elsie still would not accept that the Black Angel did not exist and had no power over her life.

'We should go to the police,' I said, though I suspected they would not be terribly interested.

'Oh no!' said Elsie. 'We mustn't do that. Going to the police would make things worse.'

'Would you like me to speak to Beryl?' I asked.

'Would you?' asked Elsie, a light of hope appearing in her eyes. 'Maybe you could explain that I haven't got any more money.'

'Where does Beryl live?' I asked.

'She lives in a cottage with a man called Ollie,' said Elsie. She told me the address.

'What does Ollie do?'

'He's horrid,' said Elsie.

'What does he do?' I asked again.

'He's just horrid,' said Elsie. 'He goes into pubs and cafés and just sits there until they give him money to go away.'

'Why would they do that?'

'Because he stares at people. He looks very fierce. He makes people feel uncomfortable. So the people who run the cafés give him money to go somewhere else.'

'Have you got somewhere you can stay for a few days?' I asked her. 'So that Beryl can't find you?'

Elsie thought for a moment. 'I can go and stay with my aunt,' she said. 'She has a boarding house but she's not full. She'd put me up for a few days. It's only round the corner from where I live but I don't think Beryl knows about it.' She told me the address.

'Go there and stay there,' I told her. And I promised Elsie that I would help her.

After Elsie had gone I sat in my surgery for over half an hour trying to think of a way in which I could keep my promise. I thought again of going to the police. But in my heart I knew that wouldn't work. For a brief moment I even thought of arranging for Thumper to take a couple of pals round to scare Beryl and her 'horrid' man away from the area. I pulled out a map and found Beryl's cottage on it. I drew a ring around the cottage in red ink and stared at it. There had to be a way to help Elsie.

And then Miss Johnson came in and told me of a call I had to make in the village. I left the map on my desk and did the call.

When I got back Thumper Robinson was waiting for me. He was sitting in the patient's chair in my surgery looking at the map I'd marked.

'I've got a load of logs in the truck,' he said. 'Do you want some?'

I said I'd take all he'd got, asked him how much he wanted. I paid him cash.

'Myrtle Cottage on Combe Road,' he said, pointing to the red ring I'd drawn on the map. 'I heard something about Combe Road and Myrtle Cottage recently. Can't for the life of me remember what it was. What do you know about Myrtle Cottage?'

'Nothing,' I told him, with a shrug. 'But I know who lives there.'

'Beryl and Ollie,' said Thumper. He put the map back down on my desk.

'Yes.'

'Nasty pair,' said Thumper. 'She dabbles in witchcraft and he's just a bully. They rent the cottage. They've lived there for years.'

'I know about the witchcraft.'

'One of them been upsetting a patient of yours?'

I nodded. 'I can't tell you who.'

Thumper shook his head. 'I don't want to know,' he said. 'But Beryl and Ollie need teaching a lesson. They've been annoying people for far too long. She pretends to be a gypsy Queen. Dabbles in witchcraft. Scares people silly.'

'I know,' I said. 'Have the police been round there?'

Thumper laughed. 'They've tried,' he said. 'Ollie just snarls at them. He's the sort of person most people apologise to when he treads on their toes. The trouble is that even when Beryl and Ollie break the law no one will give evidence against them.'

'There must be a way . . . ' I murmured.

'We could pan them,' suggested Thumper.

I frowned. 'What's that?'

'It was an old way of getting rid of people who were bad,' explained Thumper. 'All the villagers would gather outside their house. They'd be armed with pans and ladles and they'd make a noise.'

'And that would scare the bad people away?'

'It used to,' said Thumper. He paused. 'So they say.'

'Do you think it would work with Beryl and Ollie?'

Thumper smiled and shook his head. 'No,' he admitted. 'No, I don't.'

'We need to scare them,' I said.

Suddenly Thumper banged his fist on my desk. 'I've just remembered!'

'Remembered what?'

'Combe Road,' he said excitedly. 'They're widening Combe Road. It leads up to a caravan site on the cliffs and in the summer caravans are always getting stuck. So they're doing some road widening.'

'And what about Myrtle Cottage?'

'Knocking it down,' said Thumper. 'They're getting a compulsory purchase order and knocking it down.'

'How do you know?' I asked him.

'A mate of mine owns a digger. He does a lot of demolition work for the council and is always tendering for stuff. He has a contact there who tips him off about what the council is planning. It isn't public knowledge yet.'

'But surely the council will have contacted the owner of the cottage?'

'They may have done,' said Thumper. 'But

Ollie and Beryl are just renting it. The council may have contacted the owner — but that's Mickey Dunn who owns all sorts of property round there. And he won't have bothered telling Ollie and Beryl.'

'I've thought of something I could try,' I said. 'Are you sure they won't know?'

'Not for another two days,' said Thumper. 'Details of the road widening will be in the local paper on Thursday and then everyone will know.'

'I'm going round to see Ollie and Beryl,' I said, standing up.

'I'll come with you,' said Thumper.

I shook my head. 'This will work better if I go alone.'

On the way to Myrtle Cottage I rehearsed what I intended to say.

Ollie opened the door. He was as ugly and as frightening as I had heard.

I introduced myself.

'We didn't call for a doctor,' snarled Ollie.

'I know,' I said. 'But I'm here about a patient of mine called Elsie Fingleton.'

'Don't know her,' said Ollie. He tried to shut the door but I was ready for him and had my foot in the way.

'Your wife does,' I said. 'Could I have a word with her, please?'

'What about?'

'It's important,' I said.

Ollie thought for a moment and then called for Beryl.

'What is it?' she demanded when she came to the door. She was dressed entirely in black and looked older than I knew she was.

'I'm afraid you've frightened a patient of mine,' I said. 'Elsie Fingleton.'

'Never heard of her,' said Beryl, without hesitating.

'She knows you as Queen Juliana,' I said.

'So what?'

'I'd like you to stop frightening her with your superstitious nonsense,' I said. 'She hasn't got any more money.'

'If she believes it that's her look out,' said Beryl, now not bothering to deny that she knew Elsie.

'It could be a problem for you,' I said.

'Are you threatening me?' demanded Elsie.

'No, not at all,' I said. 'But I'd like you to see her and tell her that she is no longer in danger.'

Beryl laughed. 'And what are you going to do if I don't?'

This was my moment.

'I'll have your house knocked down,' I said quietly. I always find that threats muttered softly are far more menacing than threats uttered loudly.

Beryl stared at me.

I stared at her. And I smiled.

'Ollie!' she yelled.

Ollie appeared.

'This bastard is threatening to knock down our house,' she said.

'No I'm not,' I corrected her. 'I'm not going to knock down your house. The council will do it.'

'You can't do that, mate,' snarled Ollie.

And he slammed the door.

★ ★ ★

Two days later, armed with a copy of the local newspaper, I went back.

'Have you seen the paper?' I asked Ollie, who answered the door.

He stared at me. I think it was intended to be menacing. I showed him the story about the road widening. 'Your house is going to be knocked down,' I said.

'You fixed this?' he said, more astonished than anything else.

I stared at him.

'Beryl!' he yelled.

Beryl arrived. He showed her the newspaper and then looked at me. 'You've got that sort of clout?'

'I want Beryl to stop frightening my

patient,' I explained.

'So now what?' he asked. He didn't look anywhere near as frightening now.

'You've lost your home,' I told him.

'And now what?'

'You leave the area,' I said. 'But before you go, you apologise to Elsie, you give her back the money you've taken from her and you tell her that there isn't anything for her to worry about.'

They stared at me.

'Or else?' said Ollie.

I shrugged. 'I'll think of something,' I said, trying to give the impression that I had limitless powers over their lives.

They looked at each other.

'When?' asked Beryl.

I looked at my watch. 'Thirty minutes,' I said. 'Elsie's cottage.'

Ollie nodded. 'She'll be there,' he said. 'And then you'll leave us alone?'

'You leave the area and I'll leave you alone,' I assured him.

I went back to my car and climbed in behind the wheel. I had to wait for a moment or two before I drove off. I was shaking and I was sweating so much that my shirt was stuck to my back.

Beryl was there on time. She gave Elsie back her money and assured her that the

Black Angel had gone and would trouble her no more. She even apologised. And then she left.

Elsie beamed and cried a little in relief. She made a cup of tea for us both. Fifteen minutes later I left. A quarter of a mile down the road I looked in my rear view mirror and noticed Thumper Robinson's truck behind me. I pulled over, got out and walked back to where he had parked.

'Did it go OK?' he asked.

'Fine,' I said. 'Beryl and Ollie are leaving the area.'

'Great,' said Thumper.

'How did you come to be here?' I asked him.

He grinned. 'You didn't notice me before?'

'No.'

'I've been following you since you left Bilbury Grange an hour and a half ago,' he said. 'I asked Patsy to let me know when you left. I just thought I'd keep an eye on you. Ollie can be a naughty boy.'

I nodded. 'Thanks.'

'I couldn't have sorted it better myself,' he said.

It was one of the best compliments I've ever had.

Dr Brownlow's Advice

My predecessor as Bilbury's medical practitioner, Dr Brownlow, was my greatest teacher. To use a now fashionable (though old-fashioned) word he was my mentor. He was, without a doubt, the wisest man I ever knew. He taught me almost everything I know about medicine and most of what I know about life.

Over the years I got into the habit of writing down the things he told me. I put them into a small, red and black spiral-bound notebook.

I told myself I was doing this so that I could pass on these pieces of wisdom to my children. But I was really doing it so that *I* could remember his words — and remind myself of them whenever I needed reassurance or advice. Much of the advice he gave me was designed to make me a better doctor. But I think some of the advice probably works for patients too.

Here's a selection of the advice he gave me:

1. However bad things may be always remember that these are tomorrow's good old days.

2. Never complain in a restaurant before you have finished your meal.

3. Ignore those who tell you that something can't be done. All they mean by that is that they cannot do it and cannot see a way that it can be done; they do not mean that *you* cannot do it. How could they possibly know what you are capable of?

4. You will regret the things you didn't do far more than the things you did do.

5. When patients tell you things about their lives write down what they tell you on their medical notes. When they come back to see you again you can ask them how they enjoyed their holiday, how the new bathroom is coming along or how their husband is coping with his problems at work. You may remember some of these things anyway but you won't remember them all and jotting down little notes will help to give your memory a jog occasionally.

6. It's the dog you don't worry about who is the one who bites you in the leg. While you're worrying about the black dog in front of you, the white dog comes round behind you and nips you in the calf. Whatever it is that you worry most about it will almost always be something else

(usually unforseen) that causes you most trouble.

7. The more taps you have the greater the chances are that one of them will be leaking. And the more slates there are on your roof the greater the chance that one of them will slip off.

8. Look after the minutes as carefully as you look after the pennies and the hours, like the pounds, will look after themselves.

9. Life is too short to be wishy-washy. Say what you feel. Defend what you believe in. Don't waste time and energy on those whom you despise.

10. Every human body has a weak point — it may be the stomach, the lungs or the skin. When you are under too much stress, or are pushing yourself too hard, you will acquire symptoms at or around your weak point. Regard these symptoms as a warning sign to pull back a little.

11. People always appreciate a doctor who is prepared to visit — without making a song and dance about it. If you're going to do something, why whinge and make everyone feel uncomfortable about it?

12. Buy socks that are all the same colour and the same style. This will make life much easier. And who cares what colour socks you wear?

13. They used to build houses out of stone. Today, they build them out of breeze-block and then clad the visible bits with artificial stone to make it look as though the houses are made of stone. Remember this when someone argues that progress is always good.

14. Expect the worst and your life will be full of pleasant surprises.

15. Reasonable people are invariably without passions or ideas and reasonable men never do anything remarkable. Remember this when critics complain that you are being unreasonable.

16. When faced with a problem in medicine (and in life) it is sometimes best to do nothing — and to wait and see what happens. Very few doctors realise this and even fewer are prepared to act this way.

17. A doctor can often produce an improvement in a patient's condition by taking him off the drugs prescribed by other doctors.

18. Never lend money to friends.

19. When you are travelling a long distance always take advantage of every opportunity to empty your bladder.

20. Carry matches with you when visiting other people's homes or staying in hotels. Lighting a match in the lavatory may save

you considerable embarrassment.

21. As soon as you have a little money saved up, invest ten per cent of it in gold coins and keep them somewhere very safe.

22. You should only ever do things for one (or more) of three reasons: first, because it will make the world a better place for those around you; second, because it will be fun; third, for money which you can use to make life better for you and for others.

Signed By The Author

Molly Tranter had lived in London until her mid twenties. She'd arrived in Devon during the Second World War to work on a farm in Bilbury as a 'land girl' and while digging up turnips had fallen in love with Kenny, the son of a local farmer. He was a sapper, home for a long weekend leave, and they'd gone into Barnstaple together to the cinema. After he'd gone back to the front they'd written to each other. And six months after meeting Molly he came back again, this time for a slightly longer leave. During Kenny's second leave the two married. They both knew it might be their only chance. Three months later, a telegram arrived and turned Molly into a widow.

'I saw Molly Tranter today,' said Gilly, putting a new bowl of peanuts on our table. 'Haven't seen her for months. She was in Peter Marshall's shop.'

There were six of us sitting in the Duck and Puddle having an early evening drink: Thumper Robinson and his girlfriend Anne Thwaites, Patchy Fogg and his wife, Patsy and me.

'I haven't seen her for ages,' said Patsy. 'How is she?'

'Frail but surprisingly lively,' said Gilly. She picked a couple of empty glasses off the table. 'She's got a bit of a chest infection. She shouldn't have been out but you know what she's like. She was a bit down too, when I saw her. Her sister is dying. Molly wants to go and see her one last time but can't afford the rail fare.'

We all expressed sympathy. We all liked Molly Tranter.

'I don't suppose you could pop round and see if she's got anything you can sell for her?' Gilly asked Patchy.

'Of course I will,' said Patchy. 'I'll pop round now. How much does she need?'

'£50 would buy her train tickets and give her a few pounds for taxis,' said Gilly.

'OK,' said Patchy, standing. 'I'll take a look.'

'Come in my car,' I told him, standing too. 'I'll have a look at her chest while you take a peek at her antiques.'

We slipped out of the Duck and Puddle and drove round to Molly's cottage. She was surprised but pleased to see the two of us.

I listened to her chest, checked her lungs and heart, and gave her some antibiotics. 'You should have called me,' I told her. We talked about her sister while Patchy finished looking around the room.

'Is there anything you can sell for me?' Molly asked him.

'The table is pretty decent,' he said. 'I can get 250 for it.'

Molly shook her head. 'Oh, I couldn't sell that,' she said. 'My husband's family gave me that.'

'The bookcase?'

Molly looked sad. 'They gave me that too,' she said. 'I'd be very sad to sell that.'

'Let me take a look at these books,' said Patchy, opening the front of the bookcase.

'Oh you can take any of those,' said Molly. 'I never look at them.'

Patchy flicked through the books. Eventually he picked one out. 'What about this one?' he asked her.

'Oh you can take that,' said Molly. 'What's it worth?'

'I can give you £100 for it,' said Patchy.

Molly gasped in delight. 'Oh that would be wonderful!' she said.

Patchy took out his wallet, removed ten £10 notes and put them on the table in front of Molly. Like all antique dealers he always carried quite a sum around with him in his wallet. He picked up the book he'd bought from her and slipped it into his pocket.

168

'Take the rest of those capsules,' I told her. 'When are you going to see your sister?'

'I'll go early next week,' she replied. 'Now that I've got the money.'

'You should be feeling better by then,' I told her. 'Finish off all the capsules. And ring me if you don't feel better before you go.'

Molly said she would.

Outside, in the car, I looked at Patchy. 'Can I see the book?' I asked.

Patchy had stuffed it in his pocket. 'Oh, it's not particularly interesting,' he said airily.

I reached over and took the book out of his pocket.

'The Bible,' I said, reading the title. I opened the first pages and looked at the copyright page. 'Very good,' I said. 'It's the 1922 edition.'

'It's an unusual edition,' said Patchy, looking embarrassed.

'£100, eh?' I said. I put the book back into Patchy's pocket. 'I think we've got a copy like that at home.'

'Similar perhaps,' said Patchy, wriggling uncomfortably.

I started the car.

'Just keep your fingers crossed Molly doesn't tell anyone what you paid for it,' I told him. 'If she does you'll have a queue outside your door before the weekend.

Everyone in Bilbury will want to sell you their copy of the Bible for £100.'

Patchy looked worried for a moment.

'I'll tell them Molly's book was signed by the author,' he said.

Hypochondriacs and Malingerers

All the available evidence shows that the number of hypochondriacs — people who genuinely believe that they are ill when they aren't — is increasing rapidly.

Four out of every five men and six out of every seven women complain that they aren't well. Even worse, over half of all men and about three quarters of all women say that they are *never* well. And yet the evidence suggests that about half of all these prospective patients are, in fact, perfectly healthy.

We have more doctors than ever before. We are spending more money on health care. But there are also more hypochondriacs than ever before.

Why?

There are a number of explanations.

First, people are more likely to feel ill if they are bored, unhappy or frustrated. And today millions of people are bored, unhappy and frustrated. Millions don't have jobs. Millions more have jobs they hate.

Second, loneliness is becoming a greater and greater problem. We don't talk to one another enough. Talking and sharing problems really does help. You don't need a psychotherapist — the evidence shows that talking to a friend, a neighbour or even a barman or hairdresser will do. People who are lonely have too much time to think about themselves and their health. Hypochondriacs know that having an illness makes them special and gives them something to talk about that will make them the centre of attention. (The three words you should never say to a hypochondriac are 'How are you?'.)

Third, we are constantly being terrified out of our minds by exaggerated reports of new illnesses and deadly diseases.

Like all doctors I have, over the years, met a considerable number of hypochondriacs.

It may not be generally realised, however, that there are as many different varieties of hypochondriac as there are different types of cheese in France.

I have met hypochondriacs whose lives were crippled by their fears; people obsessed by their imaginary illnesses.

And I have met hypochondriacs who so much enjoyed the attention and sympathy their imaginary illnesses attracted that they became angry and upset if they were told that there was nothing the matter with them. There really are people who genuinely seem to enjoy ill health.

One hypochondriac I knew, Algernon Crabtree, positively lived for the attention his imaginary illnesses attracted. When, in frustration, I told him that he was the healthiest man I knew he was so upset that he burst into tears. He was terribly disappointed that there was nothing wrong with him. Moments later, when he had recovered, he demanded a second opinion. I remember that he used to read the obituaries in his daily newspaper to make sure he hadn't died. 'I might have died and gone to heaven,' he argued when I said that I thought this might be regarded as rather an eccentric thing to do.

It's worth making the point, of course, that at some stage in their careers all doctors become hypochondriacs. Fortunately, it's a stage that most of us grow through.

A chap I once shared a flat with was a terrible sufferer. Being a hypochondriac meant that he got everything we discussed. And once he qualified, as a junior doctor, things just got worse and worse. Every time he saw a patient he developed the patient's symptoms. His life became very miserable. His mother once sent him a calendar for

Christmas. He got very upset about it and rang her up to complain. 'It's no good you giving me a calendar,' he told her. 'I'll be dead before the year's out.'

The only time he was ever happy was when he was really ill.

'Only when I'm ill,' he said glumly, 'do I stop worrying about becoming ill.'

Eventually, he found a very effective solution. He decided to specialise in a subject where he would never again suffer from the symptoms complained about by his patients. He became a gynaecologist.

The most extreme hypochondriacs are undoubtedly the patients who are said to be suffering from Munchausen's Syndrome. Unlike most medical syndromes this disorder is not named after an earnest physician creating a little instant immortality for himself but after an entirely fictitious character called Baron Munchausen.

The Baron, allegedly a Russian nobleman, was the hero of an eponymously titled book which was published in 1785. He was renowned for exaggerating his exploits.

Munchausen's Syndrome sufferers aren't just harmless hypochondriacs. In order to get a doctor's attention they don't simply fake symptoms — they will actually make themselves ill by swallowing poisons or deliberately cutting themselves. A woman patient suffering from Munchausen's Syndrome managed to get herself admitted to 400 hospitals all over Europe — having 92 operations that she didn't need.

The best known sufferer of Munchausen's Syndrome I ever met was a patient who, it was eventually shown, managed to get himself admitted 216 times to 77 different hospitals. He managed all this in the space of 34 years. He had thousands of X-rays and blood tests and is believed to have had treatments costing well over £1,000,000. He had 23 operations and never went more than 6 months without being admitted to hospital. This remarkable patient used so many aliases that eventually doctors learned to identify him by his scars. His career is believed to have ended at the age of 75. By then he had spent around a third of his life in hospital beds and had been in more hospitals than any doctor or nurse. He undoubtedly knew more about medicine than many doctors.

Using over 20 different names he had countless tests before doctors realised that he was faking. His body was criss-crossed with the scars of operations he didn't need. I was working as a young casualty officer when I met him. A surgical registrar and I both felt suspicious because the signs and symptoms he displayed were just too perfect. He had every possible symptom listed in the medical textbooks. He was quite good-natured when we eventually succeeded in proving that he was a fake. He simply climbed out of his hospital bed, put on his clothes and tottered off to find another hospital. I discovered later that this isn't at all unusual. As soon as they suspect that doctors know they are faking, patients with Munchausen's Syndrome will usually make a miraculous recovery and discharge themselves from medical care.

In the end it wasn't our diagnostic acumen which caught him out but his own carelessness. He had complained of kidney pains — his favourite illness — and had tried to trick us by placing a pebble under his back when he was X-rayed. The pebble showed up on the X-ray as a kidney stone. It was a cleverly done trick because the stone had to be placed in precisely the right position. The con came to an end because he forgot to take the 'kidney stone' with him when he left the X-ray table.

Most patients with Munchausen's Syndrome show the first signs of the disease in their teens by falling ill suddenly and dramatically. They often manage to convince family, friends and doctors that they are ill by mixing fact and fiction. When they can't answer questions about their supposed illness they either become aggressive or else fake a sudden attack of pain. Because it's difficult and dangerous even to dismiss patients as faking (and it is something that is notoriously difficult to prove) doctors usually accept what they're told and, even when investigations show no abnormality, will often prescribe drugs or surgery 'to be on the safe side'.

Many patients with Munchausen's Syndrome are lonely and desperate for love and attention. They know from experience that they can get the attention and care they crave by faking illness. The outlook for such patients is bleak. Treatment usually involves long-term psychotherapy and isn't often successful. The best hope is usually for a sufferer to acquire responsibility for someone or something else — an animal or another human being for example.

Whereas sufferers from Munchausen's Syndrome are pretending to be ill simply because they want attention there is a category of hypochondriacs known as malingerers who pretend to be ill as a means to some other end.

The majority of experienced malingerers will give what doctors call 'organ recitals'; describing their problems in well-rehearsed detail. And they'll usually manage to fake a few interesting physical signs.

They will, for example, pretend to have a fever by rubbing the thermometer on the bedclothes or dipping it into a cup of tea. Or they'll make their gums bleed and then spit blood into their urine. One young malingerer I knew used to lick his palms to make them feel clammy.

All malingerers choose their diseases carefully.

The man who is trying to con a sick note out of his doctor doesn't want to spend the day having painful tests done. He wants the day off to go to a football match. He knows that something simple like a feigned backache will be far more likely to succeed than something complicated and threatening. Many patients pretend to be ill for specific reasons. When I was a hospital doctor I saw a patient pretending to have a heart attack. He wanted a heroin injection because he was an addict. And I once saw a patient pretending to have injured his leg at work. He came into the out-patients department wanting to claim compensation money from his employers. He said he couldn't walk but I guessed he was exaggerating slightly when, from a hospital window, I spotted him playing football with his son in the hospital car park.

Most malingerers are content with taking

off an odd day here or there. Occasionally, they may steal a week or a fortnight from work.

But I have met patients who have spent their entire lives malingering.

One woman I knew had seen private specialists on three continents. Her alleged ill health was her hobby and gave her an opportunity to travel. She always dressed well and looked ten years younger than she really was. Her unfortunate husband had to trail around behind her — and find the money for all her consultations. When I saw her she was travelling around the West Country visiting doctors wherever she wandered. I was, she told me proudly, the 112th doctor she'd seen in her life. She kept a diary in which she jotted down records of her consultations. She even gave the doctors points out of ten for courtesy, professional skill, bedside manner and so on. I wanted her to tell me how I rated but she refused to tell me so perhaps I didn't score very well.

Shortly after I first started work in Bilbury I met Thomas O'Donnell, a quintessential Irishman who complained softly that he had 'the weariness'. He lived in a small cottage and spent his days and his nights in a huge, old-fashioned wooden bed, covered by a double layer of heavy woollen blankets and a thick, richly-embroidered eiderdown. He had a small sun-faded postcard thumb-tacked to his front door inviting all callers to climb the stairs if they wanted to speak to him. Mr and Mrs Broadstone, his kindly next door neighbours looked after him devotedly. They shared the vegetables they grew in their garden, picked up his groceries and even did his cooking and laundry for him. The window in his bedroom was low, and from his bed Thomas could see a huge stretch of Bilbury and the surrounding countryside. Like everyone else in the village I treated him as an invalid. Neither Dr Brownlow nor I were ever able to find out what was wrong with him. But neither of us liked to tell him to his face that he was a fraud.

Once a year Mr O'Donnell would go to the hurling championships in Dublin. For this annual treat, a visit to a uniquely Irish game in which every man starts the match equipped with a large stick and ends it covered in his own and everyone else's blood, Mr O'Donnell would climb out of bed and put on a dark three piece heavy worsted suit, a white shirt with a stiffly starched collar and a plain, dark green tie. On the top of his head he would carefully place a smart black trilby hat. To get to Dublin he would hire Peter Marshall to take him to Barnstaple in his car.

From Barnstaple he would take the train to Exeter and from there he would catch the express to Birmingham. From Birmingham he took a plane to Dublin. Upon his return from the hurling championships Thomas would take off his suit, hang it up in his wardrobe and climb back into his bed.

I also knew of a woman who lived in a small village half way between Bilbury and Barnstaple. She had decided at the age of 14 that she didn't like work so she went to bed. And she stayed there for the next fifty years, eating chocolates and reading magazines.

Until she died at the age of 64 she was looked after by relatives, friends and a series of impatient doctors. Her life might not have been particularly fulfilling but it certainly wasn't very demanding either.

The big difference between Munchausen Syndrome sufferers and malingerers on the one hand and genuine hypochondriacs on the other is that while those in the first group pretend they are ill hypochondriacs genuinely believe that they are ill.

All the available evidence shows that the number of hypochondriacs — people who genuinely believe that they are ill when they aren't — is increasing rapidly.

Malingerers and patients with Munchausen's Syndrome were rare in Bilbury. But the village, and the practice, did have its fair share of hypochondriacs and, as a group, they created a greatly disproportionate amount of work. As any doctor will tell you, one genuine hypochondriac can generate ten times as many telephone calls and surgery visits as ten genuinely healthy and needy patients.

A friend of mine from medical school took a job as a general practitioner in Leamington Spa, a pleasant, rather leafy town in the English midlands. He once told me about an attempt he'd made to help the hypochondriacs in his practice.

With the approval of the senior partners in the practice where he worked he started a weekly Hypochondriacs Group. The senior doctors all said they desperately hoped that his scheme would work but admitted that in their hearts they knew it didn't stand a chance. The idea was that hypochondriacs could go along and talk about their personal problems and experiences in the same way that alcoholics do when they attend Alcoholics Anonymous meetings. My friend hoped that by sharing their pain, and their hopes and strengths, the patients would be able to deal with their fears in a constructive way. He also hoped that in the long-term the existence of his group would mean that the doctors in the practice would spend less time dealing with this small group of very demanding people. He thought, rather naively perhaps, that once they heard other hypochondriacs talking about their imaginary illnesses they would be embarrassed and walk away feeling full of beans.

The scheme was an absolute disaster.

The first problem was that my friend hadn't realised that many hypochondriacs love their illnesses and are, indeed, often quite proud of them. The very last thing they really want is a cure. They go to the doctor not in search of a remedy but in search of sympathy. They want the doctor to tell them that their problem is unique and that nothing can be done about it. I've known hypochondriacs become severely depressed, and demand a second, third and fourth opinion, when told that there is nothing seriously wrong with them. There are not a few doctors with private practices who make a very good living out of offering sympathy to long-term hypochondriacs. One I know, who is especially successful, tells his patients that their problems are so special that he would like to write about them in one of the medical journals. There are journals which will print articles if the author pays a fee (these journals make most of their money from drug companies anxious to have articles published extolling the virtues of their latest wonder-drug, but they are also happy to accept money from individual doctors) and so the doctor writes a page or two about Mrs X's puzzling condition and has it published. The fee he pays to have it in print is nothing compared to the fees he charges Mrs X for support and sympathy. The cost is doubtless tax deductible as an essential expense. Thrilled to see herself in print, and to have evidence confirming that her disease is very special, Mrs X buys up two dozen copies of the journal to send to her dearest and most intimate friends. She becomes a fan of the doctor for life and several of her friends make appointments to see him too.

The second problem my doctor friend faced was that all the hypochondriacs were proud of their illnesses and only wanted to talk about themselves. They wanted lots of fuss and attention. They all wanted to have the worst symptoms and the worst prognoses. They all wanted to have been closer to death than anyone else. They all wanted to have amazed and bewildered and stumped the biggest number of doctors. They all wanted to have had the most difficult surgery. And they got very jealous, and sometimes quite hysterical, when another patient started talking about his problems as though they mattered a damn.

Finally, my friend in Leamington Spa had known that because the hypochondriacs all knew lots of medical jargon they would be able to talk to one another about their various illnesses, but he hadn't realised that hypochondriacs love acquiring new symptoms and new illnesses and would, within a very short space of time, all add everyone else's diseases to their own library of ailments.

Eventually, the Hypochondriacs Group meeting fell apart when, one by one, the members sent messages to say that they were too ill to attend. My friend reported that the senior partners were furious with him. For six months after the Group folded they were spending twice as much time on their small group of hypochondriacs as they had been before the Group started. What made things particularly galling was that instead of having just one or two favourite diseases the worst hypochondriacs now had a whole textbook of symptoms and disorders. Eventually, the senior partners introduced a strict rule limiting known hypochondriacs to one fatal disease per day and a maximum of three per week.

The happiest and most successful hypochondriacs I ever knew were a couple of men called Godfrey Fame and Michael Fortune. They ran an estate agency called Fame and Fortune. (Godfrey once admitted to me that he was born Godfrey Fane and had changed his name by deed poll. Michael's surname really was Fortune. Thumper Robinson referred to them as Piles 1 and Piles 2 because, as he said, they were both a 'pain in the bum'. Patchy, slightly more tactful, described them both as suffering from 'irritable person syndrome'.)

Godfrey and Michael were both raging hypochondriacs but they shared their symptoms, their fears and their illnesses with each other. Both enjoyed having a permanent audience, and they would literally take it in turns to talk about themselves and their health problems. I could never quite work out how the rota worked but I never knew both of them to be ill at the same time so it clearly worked quite well.

When I first moved to Bilbury they told me that they were worried that I was far too young to be their doctor.

'We need someone with experience and gravitas,' Godfrey said, when warning me that he and Michael were considering moving to an older doctor with a practice in Barnstaple.

But they never did change doctors.

'We've decided to stay with you,' said

186

Michael eventually.

'Better the devil you know,' said Godfrey.

I said I was very flattered by their trust. And then, since it was Godfrey's turn to be ill, I listened and nodded as he told me why he thought he had acquired leptospirosis while cleaning the bathroom sink and how he had contracted a variant form of Lassa fever while showing a man who'd been on holiday in Africa round a house in Shirwell. He had, as usual, been to the library in Barnstaple and knew a good deal about both of these diseases. In the end, after a careful and thorough examination, I managed to persuade him that all he had wrong with him was tinea pedis (athlete's foot) and mild incipient seborrheic dermatitis (dandruff). I gave him some cream for the tinea pedis and a special shampoo for the mild incipient seborrheic dermatitis. Both men were very happy with me when they left and told me, for the 800th time, that if Patsy and I ever wanted to sell Bilbury Grange they would be happy to handle the sale for us at a very competitive rate.

Having one or two hypochondriacs in a practice is always stimulating. But one or two is plenty.

The Woman Who Was Too Busy To Die

Human bodies are extremely complicated and over the years I learned three important things about them, none of which I had been taught by lecturers or professors at my medical school.

First, I learned that no two bodies are identical and there are an infinite number of variations. Not even twins are truly identical. When I first started to study medicine I used to think how much easier it would be for us all (doctors and patients) if bodies came with an owner's manual, but the more I learned about medicine the more I realised that such a manual would have to contain so many variations, footnotes and appendices that it wouldn't fit into the British Museum let alone sit comfortably on the average bookshelf. Even if manuals were individually prepared they would still be too vast for practical use. However much we may think we know about illness and health there will always be exceptions; there will always be times when our prognoses and predictions are proved wrong.

Second, I learned that the human body has enormous, hidden strengths, and far greater power than most of us ever realise. We tend to think of ourselves as being delicate and vulnerable. But, in practice, our bodies are tougher than we imagine, far more capable of coping with physical and mental stresses than most of us realise. Very few of us know just how strong and capable we can be. Only if we are pushed to our limits do we find out precisely what we can do.

Third, I learned that our bodies are far better equipped for self-defence than most of us imagine, and are surprisingly well-equipped with a wide variety of protective mechanisms and self-healing systems which are designed to keep us alive and to protect us when we find ourselves in adverse circumstances. The human body is designed for survival and contains far more automatic defence mechanisms, designed to protect its occupant when it is threatened, than any motor car. To give the simplest of examples, consider what happens when you cut yourself. First, blood will flow out of your body for a few seconds to wash away any dirt. Then special proteins will quickly form a protective net to catch blood cells and form a clot to seal the wound. The damaged cells will release special substances into the tissues to make the area red, swollen and hot. The heat kills any infection, the swelling acts as a natural splint — protecting the injured area. White cells are brought to the injury site to swallow up any bacteria. And, finally, scar tissue builds up over the wounded site. The scar tissue will be stronger than the original, damaged area of skin.

Those were the three medical truths I discovered for myself. Over the years I have seen many examples of these three truths. But one patient always comes into my mind when I think about the way the human body can defy medical science, prove doctors wrong and exhibit its extraordinary in-built healing power.

★　★　★

I can still remember when I first met Dawn.

'The next patient is new to the village,' my receptionist, Miss Johnson, had said. 'She's renting the Bradshaw's old cottage on Parson Lane. Her name is Northolt. Mrs Dawn Northolt. The Family Practitioner Committee hasn't yet sent us her medical records.'

I'd stood up and waited for Mrs Northolt to enter. Right from the start, I always stood up when patients came in to see me for the same reason that I shook hands with them when they left, and, unlike some of my colleagues in general practice, wore a sports jacket instead of a white coat. I wanted to make patients feel comfortable and relaxed; as though they were visiting a friend rather than the doctor. However much they might hide it, most patients are a little nervous when they enter a doctor's surgery. My predecessor, Dr Brownlow, had believed that small, natural, social courtesies help eradicate the nervousness. And I'd decided to maintain the tradition. I still do.

Mrs Northolt looked to be in her early twenties, though I was to discover that she was actually just nineteen. She was short, dark haired and very pregnant. She had clearly spent a good deal of time crying.

She told me that she was eight months pregnant and that her husband had been away on an oil rig for nearly a year. When he'd returned home he had, not surprisingly, refused to believe her claim that the baby was his. He'd stormed out and gone to the pub where he'd discovered that his wife's faithlessness was well-known. The barman, an old friend of his, reported that she was known by the name 'Treacle' because she was considered by the locals to be a tart. She had never charged for her favours, the barman had reported, but she had, nevertheless, been exceedingly liberal with them.

'I was lonely and frightened, especially at night,' was all Dawn could offer in her defence. 'It was the only way I could get men to stay with me.'

Her husband, who had regularly sent money home, was not impressed with his young wife's explanation. He did not hit her or even shout at her. He simply packed his bags and walked out.

Desperate, even more lonely and even more frightened, Dawn also left their home in Newcastle. She had no idea who the father was. There were a number of candidates. She didn't love any of them, or even know their last names. She packed one suitcase (all she could carry) and caught a bus to Taunton, where she had an aunt. The aunt provided a bed for two nights and then found Dawn a cottage to rent. The cottage was in Bilbury. Neither of them had ever heard of Bilbury. Dawn's aunt drove her there in her Ford and then went straight back to Taunton. Once again Dawn was on her own.

★　★　★

For the first few weeks Dawn was, I remember, a lot of trouble. Since Miss

Johnson and I were the only people in the village whom she knew, she would telephone the surgery three or four times a day. She even telephoned in the evenings and at night. Once, I remember, she telephoned at midnight in a terrible state.

'What's the matter?' I asked her.

'I think I've drowned my baby!' she cried, between sobs.

'You haven't had the baby yet,' I pointed out.

'No. But I had a bath!' she told me. It had suddenly occurred to her that in taking a bath she might have drowned the baby in her womb. It took me fifteen minutes to persuade her that there was nothing for her to worry about.

★ ★ ★

She had a low opinion of doctors. She didn't like them and she didn't trust them. It wasn't difficult to see why, or to blame her.

Her previous GP, having decided that she was mentally ill, had once sent her to see a psychiatrist.

'He said I was mad,' she said.

'Who did?'

'My GP. He sent me to see a psychiatrist.'

Dawn reached over and picked up a toy

car. My desk is always littered with toys as well as books, letters and medical instruments. I put the toys there to amuse the children, though they seem to amuse the adults too. She turned it over and examined the underside. 'I thought I was ugly and useless,' she said 'At school I was always the last but one person to be picked when the captains were picking their netball and hockey teams.'

'Last but one is not too bad. You could have been the last choice.'

'The one they always picked last weighed 12 stones, had asthma and wore spectacles with lenses as thick as the bottoms of milk bottles. She had bad breath and was loathed because she never stopped telling us all how rich her family was.'

'So what did the psychiatrist say?'

'He told me to lie down on his couch and then he sat there and told me to talk about myself.'

'Did it help?'

'No.'

'Why not?'

'Because after twenty minutes or so I had run out of things to say. I lay there in silence. He didn't say a word. Twice a minute I looked at the clock. When my fifty minutes were up I asked if I should go but he didn't reply. I turned round and thought he was dead. His eyes were closed, his hands were folded across his stomach and his chin was resting on his chest. There was a long dribble of saliva connecting his chin to his cardigan. I sat up and realised that he was still breathing.'

'What was wrong with him?'

'He'd fallen asleep.'

I looked down at my desk, embarrassed for her, despite the time that had passed by since it had happened.

'Not the best thing for someone who felt inadequate,' she said softly.

'What did you do?'

'I asked him if I could go. I had to reach out and touch his shoulder to wake him up.'

'Was he embarrassed?'

'No, not at all. He told me to make another appointment to see him in a week's time.'

'Did you?'

She shook her head. 'I never saw him again.'

'Did your GP ask you what had happened?'

She shook her head again.

'What did he do?'

'He always just asked me questions about my sex life. He seemed to find it interesting. In the end I just made stuff up. I wasn't going to tell him all my personal and private thoughts. So I made stuff up.'

'Why did you keep going to see him?'

'I wanted the tranquillisers he gave me. He wouldn't give me the prescriptions if I didn't go and see him.'

★ ★ ★

'Do you think I'm mentally ill?' she asked me one day. She'd had the baby, a beautiful little girl, and had defied the social workers, who wanted her to give the child up for adoption. But, to me, she'd never really seemed to bond with the child.

I looked at her and spoke slowly and certainly, so that she would know that I knew what I was saying.

'No,' I told her. 'You're not mentally ill.'

'So, what's wrong with me?'

'You need a purpose,' I told her.

To this day I still have no idea why I said that. I would never normally say something so crass and simplistic to a patient. I've always believed that, as a GP, my job is to look after the mental and physical welfare of my patients. That's it. It isn't my place to offer advice (other than a suggestion to stop smoking or lose weight) any more than it is to make judgements.

'What do you mean?' she asked.

'You've got a baby and a new home,' I said. 'You're lucky enough to be living in a village where people treat their neighbours according to who they are, not who they were or who they ought to be. You've got a lot to be proud of and a lot to look forward to.' I remember knowing that I was way out of order. It wasn't my place to say any of this but I said it anyway. I was beginning to sound like a social worker or a newspaper agony aunt.

'What have I got to look forward to?' she asked. There was a touch of defiance in her voice.

'Watching your little girl grow up. Turning your cottage into a home for you both. Enjoying the seasons in Bilbury.'

She looked at me thoughtfully.

'You've got a decent sized garden,' I pointed out, 'you could start growing your own vegetables. If you grow too many for the two of you, you could sell the excess to Peter Marshall at the village shop.'

'I don't know anything about gardening,' she said.

'That's no problem. Your neighbours know. Ask them.'

'I don't know anyone,' she said.

I turned round to the bookshelf behind me, found the book I was looking for and handed it to her.

She took the book and read the title out loud. 'The Beginners Guide To Gardening.'

'It's the book I used when I first came to Bilbury,' I told her. 'Borrow it for as long as you like.'

Six months later she brought me a basket of home grown vegetables. The book, neatly wrapped and with a thank you card tucked inside, was at the bottom of the basket.

*   *   *

Three years after that Dawn was well settled. Her little girl was growing and healthy and Dawn, who had made several friends and was popular, was making a living working as a part time barmaid at the Duck and Puddle and selling vegetables to the village shop.

And then she came to see me one day complaining that she had found a lump in her left armpit.

'I don't know why I still bother, because I never wear sleeveless dresses and I never go out, but I was shaving,' she said. 'And I found this lump.'

I looked and felt and didn't like the feel of it. I examined her breasts and found another lump. A bigger one. This one was on the outer edge of her left breast.

'I want you to see someone,' I told her. I

picked up the telephone and made an appointment for her to see a surgeon in Barnstaple. A surgeon who specialised in women with breast cancer. She said her neighbour would look after her child for the day.

At 12.15 p.m. the following day the surgeon rang to tell me that he was taking Dawn into the operating theatre. At 1.30 p.m. he rang to tell me that there was nothing he could do for her. Dawn's breast cancer had spread and was inoperable. A day later Dawn was back home. She'd been told that she had, at most, six months to live.

'Do you remember once telling me that I needed purpose in my life?' she asked me.

I confessed that I did. 'It was very pompous of me,' I said, apologetically.

'No, no,' she said. 'It changed my life. But if I'd been told then what I've been told today I would have welcomed it,' she said. 'I didn't have anything to live for.'

I didn't say anything.

'I can't die,' she said suddenly. 'I've got everything to live for now. A lovely daughter. A real home. And friends. I'm too busy to die!'

I honestly didn't know what to say. It never, ever gets any easier. 'I'll help you in any way I can,' I told her.

'I'm not going to die,' she said. 'I can't die. Not now.'

'OK,' I said. 'Then what are you going to do to make sure it doesn't happen?'

She turned the question round. 'What would you do?'

I thought about the question and the answer. And I told her. 'I would drink lots of vegetable and fruit juices and eat lots of vegetables,' I told her. 'There's evidence to show that diet can help beat cancer.'

'OK,' she said. 'I can easily do that. What else? Would a healer help?' Suddenly, she seemed so very, very strong. I would never have believed that she would have found so much inner strength.

'Maybe,' I agreed. 'It wouldn't do any harm.'

'I heard of a healer who lives in Lynmouth,' said Dawn. 'I'll ring her. What else?'

I talked to her about visualisation. 'Imagine your body is full of tiny warriors fighting the cancer cells,' I said. 'It sounds crazy but there's some evidence to show it can work.'

'I'll try it,' she said. 'I'll do it,' she corrected herself. She looked at me. 'I'm not going to die.'

'No,' I said. 'I don't believe you are.' I promised to think of other things she could try.

A year later I had a telephone call from the surgeon who had seen her in Barnstaple.

'Do you remember that girl you sent me? Dawn Northolt?'

I said I did.

'She's just been in the clinic,' he said. 'For her check up.'

'How is she doing?'

'She should be dead,' said the surgeon. 'A year ago she had a few months to live. She had secondaries everywhere. Her blood tests were awful. She was so ill we didn't even see any point in starting her on chemotherapy.'

'She looks quite well doesn't she?' I said. I had seen her the day before and been impressed by her vitality. I had never seen her look so full of life.

'Quite well?' he said. 'She is a walking miracle. The cancer seems to be receding. I've been a surgeon for thirty years and I've never seen anything like it.'

★ ★ ★

That all happened some years ago.

I saw Dawn last week. She's fine. Her little girl is growing up into a beautiful young woman. And Dawn is healthy again.

'Do you remember that speech you gave me?' asked Dawn. 'The one about having purpose?'

'I do,' I admitted, embarrassed by the memory, as I always am.

'I found my purpose,' she said. 'Beating the cancer so that I could see my little girl grow up.'

I nodded.

'It embarrasses you when I remind you about that, doesn't it?'

I nodded.

'You shouldn't be embarrassed,' she said. 'I was the right person to say it to, it was the right thing to say, and you said it at the right time.'

It made me feel a little better.

What Would We Do Without Progress?

Thumper Robinson, Patchy Fogg and I spent an hour in the Duck and Puddle reminiscing. Here's a list of the good things we remembered from our pasts.

1. A man with a huge suitcase used to travel door-to-door selling brushes. He invariably wore a dodgy mackintosh and a trilby hat. Our mothers always used to buy brushes from him. He used to hand out small plastic toys which we loved.
2. Another man, this time with a briefcase but also wearing a dodgy mackintosh and a trilby hat, used to call round once a week to collect a few pence in insurance. He called whatever the weather. None of us could work out how the amounts he collected could have been worth collecting.
3. School children all wore ugly school uniforms.
4. It took five minutes for the television set to warm up. At the end of the evening,

transmissions would close down. They would then play God Save the Queen and loyal citizens would stand up. When you turned off the set there would be a white spot visible on the screen for some time afterwards.

5. Mums were waiting at home when their children got back from school. Even quite small children were trusted to get home safely by themselves — either walking or on bicycles.

6. In between programmes the BBC used to show a film of a potter making a pot or waves breaking on the shore.

7. Women always wore suspender belts to hold up their stockings.

8. Men wore jackets and ties, and hats too, when they went to watch cricket or football matches.

9. Women had their hair permed and wore dresses which swished when they walked.

10. Petrol station attendants cleaned car windscreens without being asked and asked the driver if he wanted the oil checked. They operated the petrol pump and took the money while the driver and his passengers remained sitting in the car. If your tyres needed air they did that too — free of charge.

11. All sorts of goods came with Green

Stamps which could be saved in a book and exchanged for exciting products. You didn't have to spend a million pounds to get something worthwhile.

12. Small items (particularly sweets) were sold in white paper bags. Large objects were placed in brown paper bags.

13. If you wrote and complained about something the company would send you a present and a letter of apology signed by someone really important. The best presents came from Cadburys.

14. Teenagers going on a date would think themselves fast and daring if they held hands in the cinema and kissed each other good night at the end of their evening.

15. Motorists would leave their cars unlocked and their car keys in the ignition when they went into a shop.

16. Screws were sold singly and loose. The ironmonger would put them into a small paper bag.

17. Girls tucked their skirts into their navy blue knickers in order to play netball in the schoolyard. The hoops never had any nets. Boys never played netball.

18. Going out to dinner was a treat kept for birthdays and special occasions and always involved sitting down at a table

with cutlery, tablemats, cloth napkins and a menu. The bill would be paid with crisp notes taken from a leather wallet and plastic would play no part in the proceedings.

19. You could buy a replacement blade for a motor car windscreen wiper — instead of having to buy a whole unit.

20. Pots and jars were easy to open. Since no one had ever tried to poison people they didn't know, no one worried about such things. Shrink-wrap had yet to be invented.

21. Sardines were sold in tins which were opened with special keys which required a knack.

22. Boys played with weapons (such as peashooters, cap guns, catapults made out of twigs and rubber bands and bows with home made arrows which flew huge distances but not necessarily in the right direction) while girls played with dolls. Children never needed batteries for their toys. Toys lasted for ever and didn't break down.

23. Conkers were fashionable in the autumn because that was when they were available. But other toys (such as hula hoops and yoyos) which were not dependent on nature also came in and out of fashion though no one ever knew quite why.

24. Milk was delivered daily by a man driving

an almost silent milk float. Imaginative milkmen also sold eggs and orange juice, though this was considered rather daring.

25. Children used to swim in rivers without worrying about pollution or drowning.

26. Films shown in cinemas were preceded by B movies, newsreel features and travel programmes.

27. You could dial telephone numbers by using letters as well as numbers. The best-known telephone number in the country belonged to Scotland Yard. The number was Whitehall 1212.

28. People made decisions by going eeny meeny miney moe.

29. Boys would fix a cigarette card onto their bicycle so that the card hit the spokes as the wheel went round and made a sound like a motorbike.

30. Summers were always long and warm (though never too hot) and it always snowed in the winter.

'Those were the days,' said Thumper, when we'd finished our list.

'All just memories now,' said Patchy. 'Thanks to progress.'

'What would we do without progress?' asked Thumper.

The Brothers

Paul and Freddie were brothers. I could never remember which was the eldest but there wasn't much between them. They were both in their mid-forties when I first arrived in Bilbury. They lived on a small farm on the outskirts of the village and kept themselves to themselves. They drove into Barnstaple once a month to do their shopping (unlike just about everyone else in the village I don't think they ever patronised Peter Marshall's village store) but grew all their vegetables themselves. Their meat they obtained by killing their own animals. They had never been in the Duck and Puddle or the village hall.

They had managed their farm themselves ever since their parents had died in a car crash when they were in their teens, and they were both known to be slightly eccentric. They didn't approve of bureaucrats or officialdom and didn't believe in paying car taxes, property taxes or income taxes. They didn't trust banks and so didn't have a bank account. They dealt only in cash. If they were shopping for cattle they would often turn up at auctions with several thousand pounds in their pockets.

There were all sorts of stories about the brothers but I had been living in Bilbury for a year before I actually met them. Late one Saturday evening Freddie arrived at Bilbury Grange in their ancient Land Rover to tell me that his brother needed help. I knew who he was as soon as I saw him. Freddie was six foot five inches tall and, as a result of a long-standing thyroid condition which he had steadfastly refused to have treated, had staring eyes. It wasn't his height or his eyes which made him unmistakeable but the fact that he never went anywhere without a double-barrelled shotgun cradled in his arms.

I got my bag and followed him back to their farm in my own car which was, at the time, still the old Morris I had bought when I'd first arrived in Bilbury. The track down to their farm had deep ruts in it and half way there, the bottom of the car started to get stuck. I had to stop, abandon the car and follow the rest of the way on foot. When he saw what had happened Freddie slowed down enough to enable me to jump onto the towing bracket on the back of his Land Rover.

Paul had cut himself with a sharp scythe. He'd very nearly severed his foot from his leg and things were a terrible mess. He'd hopped into the living room and there was blood absolutely everywhere. When I got there he was lying on the sofa watching television. He'd used a piece of old sheet and a vast quantity of orange baler twine to fix the foot back into place.

'You need to be in hospital,' I told him.

'I don't want no hospital,' said Paul.

'You have to go into hospital,' I told him.

'He don't want to go to hospital,' said Freddie who was still holding the double-barrelled shotgun and who always gave the impression that he wasn't carrying the gun as a prop.

'So let's treat him here,' I agreed.

I spent the next two hours cleaning the wound and sewing Paul's foot back into position. Luckily the bone was broken quite neatly and it wasn't difficult to get the two ends aligned. I used so much suture material that I had to go back to Bilbury Grange to fetch some more. I did so much sewing that my fingers were numb with exhaustion by the time I'd finished. At one point I even found myself contemplating borrowing a little hand held battery driven sewing machine which I knew Patsy had. But I didn't. I did the whole thing by hand and when I'd finished it didn't look a bad job. I didn't have any plaster of Paris and so I had to use heavy duty strapping to hold the leg in position. It was very much an improvised solution but it seemed to work and the brothers seemed happy enough.

I went back once and sometimes twice a day for a week and Paul made an astonishing recovery. Their farmhouse was filthy dirty but I suppose Paul must have been immune to the bugs they had. Outside bugs probably just couldn't survive in all that squalor. I remember them constantly offering me cups of tea and me having to think up fresh reasons why I couldn't accept their hospitality. I'd seen the way they just took dirty cups out of the sink, gave them a quick rinse and then used them again.

By the time Paul was able to walk again the brothers and I had become good friends. Indeed, I think I was just about the only 'stranger' they didn't regard with suspicion.

The brothers farmed about fifty acres of land and in addition to their farmhouse they also owned several barns, most of which were in a pretty dilapidated condition.

One day the brothers were out checking on their animals (they were conscientious farmers and treated all their animals well) when they discovered that three squatters had settled into one of their barns. The squatters had set up a stove and had clearly settled in for a long stay. If they'd simply been spending the night there I don't think the brothers would have objected.

'What you doing here?' demanded Paul.

'We're living here,' said the oldest and tallest squatter, a surly, arrogant youth in his early twenties.

'You can't live here!' said Paul. 'This is our barn.'

'What you going to do about it?' demanded the squatter. 'Are you going to fetch the police? They won't do anything.'

'The barn door had a padlock on it!' said Freddie. 'You broke it.'

'It fell off,' said the oldest squatter. He then made the mistake of laughing. Like most of us the brothers didn't like being laughed at, especially by strangers. But unlike most of us they didn't have to put up with it.

'Shoot 'em, Freddie!' said Paul. 'Shoot 'em!'

Freddie lifted up the shotgun but then hesitated. The squatters stared aghast.

'Shoot em!' screamed Paul.

'But which ones?' demanded Freddie. 'There are three of 'em and I've only got two barrels!'

Paul didn't have time to decide. The three squatters left. They abandoned their stove, their sleeping bags, their rucksacks, their supply of marijuana and the remainder of their clothes and ran away as fast as they could go.

Satisfied, Paul and Freddie dragged the abandoned belongings out into the open, lit a bonfire and burnt everything that had been left behind.

I found out about all this when the squatters called in at Bilbury Grange requesting medical help. All three of them were still shaking with fear when I saw them.

'We want tranquillisers,' said one.

'And sleeping tablets,' said another.

'Those two mad bastards should be locked up!' said the third.

'We're going to see the police in Barnstaple,' said the biggest.

'What's your complaint?' I asked.

They told me what had happened. 'Threatening people with a shotgun is illegal!' they said.

'They didn't shoot you?'

'Well, no . . . '

'Did the gun go off?'

They looked at one another. 'Not exactly.'

'So you don't even know that the gun was loaded?'

The biggest squatter frowned. 'What do you mean?'

'They could have been bluffing,' I said. 'I

happen to know they've got a licence for the gun. If you go to the police you would undoubtedly be the ones in trouble. It sounds to me as though you could be arrested for breaking and entering.'

Muttering loudly about not coming back to Bilbury in a hurry the three squatters left. And they left without the tranquillisers and sleeping tablets they had demanded.

The Stowaway

Some people make friends when they travel. I have an acquaintance who can't pop into the local supermarket without finding new chums to add to his formidable Christmas card list. If he goes for a walk in a deserted park he will somehow come back with half a dozen new chums. I'm not good at making friends. Too shy, I suppose. But everywhere I go I meet cats and now, I'm proud to say, I have cat friends everywhere. One of the good things about having cats as friends is that they demand nothing and expect nothing. (Obviously, cats who have become 'family' expect a great deal and demand more.) And it's easy to meet new cats.

I always seem to find affectionate cats in churches and churchyards. I have met and had long, meaningful conversations with cats in churches all over England. I don't know what it is about cats in such places but they seem to me to be almost as keen to make new human acquaintances as I am to make new cat acquaintances.

Over the years many things have happened to convince me that cats know far more than they are letting on, and have a much greater control over our lives than they are admitting to.

For example, a year or so ago one of my patients, Mrs Porter, an elderly widow, asked me if I knew someone who might accept a job as her companion and live-in nurse. For nearly a decade after her husband's death, Mrs Porter had shared her home and her life with a kind and considerate Spanish nurse who had looked after her with far more genuine affection than could normally be expected from a paid employee.

'Maria has to go back to Spain,' explained Mrs Porter sadly. 'Her mother has died and she has to take care of her father. As the only unmarried daughter she feels she has no choice.'

Both women were heartbroken. Maria liked her employer and enjoyed living in Bilbury. She really didn't want to go back to Spain. And Mrs Porter was frightened of a future without Maria. A stroke some years earlier had left her unable to look after herself without a considerable amount of practical care and she was, I knew, terrified that if she couldn't find a suitable replacement she would have no choice but to find a room in a nursing home. And, since there weren't any nursing homes in Bilbury that would mean leaving the village where she had spent almost the whole of her life and wherein lived every friend she had in the world.

'I have to go into Barnstaple to renew my car tax,' I told her. 'Would you like me to call into the Labour Exchange to see if they have anyone suitable on their books?'

She said she would and so, the following day, I found myself sitting on an uncomfortable plastic chair being quizzed by a dour, weedy man in his 60s with a military haircut and sinus problems.

'You won't find anyone prepared to live in,' he said. 'Not these days. What about a team of nurses?'

'A team?'

'You'd need at least six to cover nights, weekends and holidays,' he said.

'That would cost a fortune!' I protested. 'And there wouldn't be any continuity.'

'You won't find anyone prepared to live in and work those sort of hours,' insisted the dour little man. 'Not these days. People know their rights.'

'It's the sort of job that would suit a middle-aged woman looking for a pleasant home and light nursing duties,' I explained.

'We don't have anyone like that,' sniffed the man, flicking aimlessly through a plastic box containing a number of file cards. 'You're about a century too late.'

I left the Labour Exchange feeling terribly gloomy.

I visited the Post Office and renewed the car tax, took two books back to the public library for Patsy, picked up a piece of curtain material for her mother, picked up a supply of dressings that one of the pharmacies had ordered for me, collected a piece of glass that Patchy had ordered cut to size for a picture he was reframing and headed back to the car park. On the way I had to pass one of Barnstaple's oldest churches. I have almost as much difficulty passing old churches as I have passing second hand book shops.

I sat in a pew in the cool and empty church for a few minutes and informally asked God if he would mind doing what He could to prove the sniffy clerk at the Labour Exchange wrong. I try not to ask Him to do too much for me, but I'm never averse to asking Him to do something for a friend or for one of my patients.

Outside the church, I saw a black cat rubbing itself against the gate into the churchyard. I bent down to stroke its head and the cat ignored me completely, moving slightly out of reach each time I tried to touch it. I was in something of a hurry because I had about three minutes left on my car park ticket so I stood up and started to move away. The cat immediately stopped rubbing itself against the gate and ran after me. He then stood still while we got to know each other a little better.

'Sorry, young fellow,' I said, glancing at my watch, 'but if I don't go now I'll get a penalty ticket in the car park.' I don't know where they hide but the council's team of car park attendants always spot within seconds if I'm parked with an expired ticket.

The cat followed me and despite my repeated attempts to persuade him to go back to where I'd found him he insisted on following me all the way to the car park.

'You really must go back!' I insisted, as I packed my purchases into the boot of the car. I wrapped Patchy's glass in between the curtain material and an old rug I keep in the boot. When I'd finished I looked around for the cat and saw, to my relief, that he'd disappeared. We were only a short walk from the church and I was confident he would have found his way back without too much difficulty. Barnstaple was much quieter in those days than it is now.

When I got back home and opened the boot lid I had the surprise of my life to see the cat sitting comfortably inside the boot and looking up at me with a big grin on his face.

My first reaction, I'm afraid, was anger. I was quite cross with him. 'Now I'll have to go back into Barnstaple!' I told him.

The road from Bilbury to Barnstaple is winding, narrow and slow. If you drive at a normal pace it takes just over half an hour. If you drive like a madman it takes just under half an hour. So taking the cat back into Barnstaple was going to take me an hour.

I unloaded the stuff out of the boot and carried it and the cat into the kitchen.

'Where did you find that one?' asked Patsy, who loves cats just as much as I do.

I explained.

'He's probably thirsty,' said Patsy. She poured him a saucer of milk and then told me that there had been two calls for me. Neither of them was urgent but neither of them could wait until I got back from my unscheduled trip to Barnstaple.

'I'll have to leave the stowaway here,' I told her. 'I'll take him back later.'

But the calls took longer than I had expected and by the time I got back to the house it was half past nine and I was worn out.

'I'll take him back into Barnstaple in the morning,' I said. 'After surgery and before I do the visits. I hope no one misses him.'

We fed him, gave him more milk,

introduced him to Sophie and Emily and found him a blanket and a quiet corner of the house which he could call his own. He knew how to use the cat flap and, although Patsy and I were at first concerned that he might get lost, it quickly became clear that he was not the sort of cat who needs to have his paws buttered to persuade him not to stray.

In the morning, after I'd finished the surgery and completed the most urgent of the day's calls, I popped our stowaway into a cat basket and took him back to Barnstaple.

Patsy and I had agreed that the most sensible thing would be to take him back to the church where I'd found him and to release him there. But when I arrived back at the church I couldn't help noticing a large notice taped onto the oak door.

Below the words 'CAT LOST' and a picture of the stowaway there was a sad message offering a reward of £5 for information leading to his recovery. And there was, of course, a telephone number to call.

I found a telephone kiosk and made the call.

'Are you the person who has lost a cat?' I asked, when the phone was answered. The woman doing the answering had clearly been sitting right next to the receiver.

'Yes. This is Mrs Stokes. Have you found

him?' There was no name on the notice.

'I have,' I told her. 'He's safe and sound.' I tried to explain what had happened but the woman was too excited to take in my rather complicated story.

'Where are you?' she demanded.

'Outside the church.'

'I'll be three minutes.'

She was there in two. A woman in her fifties. About five foot tall and wiry. She wore a black skirt, a brown jumper, black stockings and a pair of brown, sensible looking slippers. She had clearly rushed straight out of the house without bothering to put on her shoes. She was carrying her purse.

'He's in here,' I said, pointing to the cat carrier.

She bent down, fiddled with the catch and opened the door at the front of the carrier. The stowaway emerged. Cat and owner seemed delighted to see each other. It was impossible to tell which was the most excited of the two.

'What's his name?' I asked, after allowing them time to give each other cuddles and licks. (The woman did the cuddling and the cat did the licking.)

'Timothy,' replied the woman. 'I call him Timmy.'

'I'm so sorry about what happened,' I said.

She looked at me, slightly confused. I explained again about how I'd come to take Timothy to Bilbury.

'Oh, that's all right,' she said. 'Not your fault.' Still clutching her beloved cat she fumbled with her purse. 'I owe you five pounds,' she said.

I held up a hand. 'Of course you don't!' I said, laughing with embarrassment.

'But your time and the petrol,' she said. 'Five pounds isn't nearly enough.'

'I'm just delighted that you've found each other,' I told her. To be honest, just watching their mutual delight was reward enough.

'Well, at least come back with us and have a cup of tea before you head back to Bilbury,' she said. I hesitated. 'We won't take 'No' for an answer, will we Timmy?'

'OK, thanks,' I said. I knew we wouldn't have to go far. And we didn't. We walked down a narrow lane behind the church and I found myself in a small, private part of the town I never knew existed. A tiny piece of heaven. Her home was a small terraced cottage. One of six. The cottage had a front garden that looked like one of those photographs with which large, expensive boxes of chocolates always used to be adorned. Foxgloves, cornflowers, nasturtiums and so on.

She led the way into a parlour with a ceiling so low I had to bend my neck in order to stand upright.

'I'll just give Timmy a little chicken, and then I'll put the kettle on,' she said. She opened the fridge, took out a plate and unwrapped the remains of half a cooked chicken. She took a knife and cut several slices from the breast of the chicken and arranged them neatly on a plate. It was, I noticed, a nice piece of Royal Albert china that matched the saucer that already contained milk and the cup full of fresh water. I felt rather guilty. Our cats always eat off odd bits of china that have been passed down from dining room service. Timmy was purring loudly long before the chicken had been cut. Once Timmy had been fed Mrs Stokes put the kettle on. While it boiled she took Royal Albert cups and saucers out of one cupboard and a metal cake tin out of another cupboard.

'Would you like a piece of sponge cake?' she asked. 'I haven't got any other I'm afraid. But I do have ginger biscuits if you prefer.'

'A piece of sponge cake would do very nicely, thank you,' I told her.

As we drank our tea and ate generous helpings of an excellent, light sponge cake Mrs Stokes asked me about Bilbury. I told her it was a village about half an hour from Barnstaple and explained that if she had never been there that was no great surprise because we tended to keep ourselves to ourselves and most people in North Devon didn't know where it was.

'I've always envied people who live in villages,' she told me. 'I've spent all my life here in the town but I've always thought how lovely it would be to have a quiet life in a rural community.'

'Barnstaple is hardly a big city!' I remarked light heartedly. 'And you live in a very quiet part of it. I didn't know this place existed.'

'It is very pleasant,' said Mrs Stokes. 'Timmy and I will be sorry to leave.'

'Why on earth are you leaving?' I asked. I took another bite of the home-made cake. It really was very splendid.

'Not our choice,' said Mrs Stokes. 'They're knocking these houses down to extend the shopping centre.' She nodded towards my plate. 'Would you like another piece?'

'Oh no!' I cried, in genuine horror. 'That's awful.' I suddenly realised what I'd said. 'Not the cake!' I said hurriedly. 'The cake is wonderful but I mustn't have another piece. I should be getting back.'

'I'm just glad my husband isn't alive to see it happen,' said Mrs Stokes. 'He lived here all his life. He was born here.'

'Can they do that?' I asked, putting my plate on the table and standing up. 'Just throw you out?'

'I'm afraid so,' said Mrs Stokes. 'It seems they can do whatever they want these days.'

I said how sorry I was to hear it and asked if she'd found somewhere to go.

'I'll probably go up to Lancashire,' said Mrs Stokes. 'I have a nephew up there. He says he can find me an old person's flat not too far from where he lives. It's on the 11th floor.' She looked very glum. 'I'll have to retire, of course but it's only another year to the pension so I suppose it's about time.'

'What about Timmy?' I asked. 'Can you take him?'

'I won't go if he can't go,' she said defiantly. 'My nephew is making enquiries.'

'What work do you do now?' I asked.

'I work at the Grand,' she told me, naming a large hotel in the town centre. 'It's very handy. I clean the rooms after the guests. Make the beds. That sort of thing.'

It was only then that I thought of Mrs Porter. I sat down again. 'Maybe I will have another piece of your wonderful cake,' I told her. 'There's something I'd like to talk to you about.'

And so a month later Mrs Stokes and

Timmy moved to Bilbury.

Was my meeting with Timmy purely serendipitous? Or is it possible that the cat knew exactly what he was doing when he climbed into my car boot?

Woody Bay Flotsam

At five minutes past nine I got fed up of waiting for the first patient to come in, opened my door and went out into my receptionist's office.

'Where are the patients?' I asked Miss Johnson.

'There aren't any, doctor,' she replied.

I stared at her and frowned. 'We can't have cured everyone!'

'There's no one here,' she said. 'Do you want me to bring the letters in for you to look through?'

Every morning, after the surgery, I would go through the morning mail and, where necessary, dictate replies for Miss Johnson to type up in the afternoon.

'It's Monday morning!' I said.

'Yes, doctor.'

'Monday is always busy.'

'Yes, doctor. But there was a shipwreck during the night.'

I stared at her, frowning. 'I'm sorry,' I said. 'Did you say there was a shipwreck during the night?'

'I did, doctor,' she said. 'In Woody Bay.'

I walked over to the wall and looked at the calendar. 'This is 1972?'

'It is.' She opened an envelope, threw the envelope away and put the letter it had contained onto the growing pile on her desk. It was a hospital letter, from a consultant, about one of my patients.

'We haven't drifted through a time warp? We haven't gone back to 1872.'

'No, doctor.' She picked up another envelope and set to work with the letter opener again.

'A shipwreck?'

'Yes.'

'Not caused by men with lanterns seducing an unfortunate ship's captain onto the rocks?'

'No. A freighter. It ran onto the rocks near Woody Bay during the night.'

'And that's why we don't have any patients?'

'Everyone has gone down to the wreck.'

'Tell me they're not searching the shore for flotsam and jetsam?'

'I think they probably are, I'm afraid.' She repeated the exercise with the envelope. 'Do you know the difference between flotsam and jetsam?'

'I looked them up when I knew I was going to live in a village populated by pirates and wreckers,' I told her. 'Flotsam is wreckage that floats. And bits of stuff that fall into the water and float. Jetsam is stuff that is jettisoned and gets washed ashore.'

'But jetsam doesn't float?'

'I assume not.'

'So how does it get ashore?'

'I have no idea. Maybe it does float. Actually, I suppose it must float.'

'So jetsam is just flotsam that was put there on purpose?'

I took the letter opener from her. 'Miss Johnson,' I said firmly. 'This is a fascinating, semantic discussion but I'm more interested in what is happening than in how we describe it. There are moral questions here.'

'I don't think anyone was out there with lanterns,' said Miss Johnson. 'And if the stuff was deliberately thrown overboard surely people have a right to pick it up.'

I hesitated. I had a feeling I was losing the argument.

'If the stuff is left there it will become litter and make the shoreline look untidy.'

I sighed. 'I'm going to take a look,' I said.

'Mind you only pick up the jetsam,' Miss Johnson said firmly. 'Leave the flotsam where it is so that the ship's owner can collect it later.'

It took me twenty minutes to get to Woody Bay. The cliffs were packed with cars. Lines of villagers from Bilbury, Combe Martin, Ilfracombe, Kentisbury, Trentishoe, Lynton, Parracombe, Bittadon, Martinhoe and a dozen other small towns and villages were making their way down to the shore. The cliffs around there are steep and the paths that exist are rocky and treacherous. There was still quite a wind blowing and the sea could be heard crashing onto the rocks.

Thumper and Patchy were there, of course.

'What's going on?' I asked.

'Freighter ran ashore,' said Thumper. 'We came to see if anyone needed help.'

I looked at him.

He shrugged. 'And to see what had been washed ashore,' he said.

'The crew were all taken off in the night,' said Patchy. 'It was on the radio.'

'Were they all OK?' I asked.

'Not a scratch,' said Patchy.

'All a bit disappointing,' said Thumper.

'We were hoping there might be a few cases of whisky,' said Patchy.

'Whisky Galore,' said Thumper.

'I've read the book and seen the film,' I told him.

'Of course, gold coins would have been better but gold has a tendency to sink,' said Patchy.

'No whisky?' I asked.

'Sadly no,' said Patchy.

'The freighter was coming from China,' said Thumper. 'Loaded with 80,000 bras.'

I laughed. 'You're joking!'

'Sadly, I am not,' said Thumper. Someone I didn't recognise hurried past carrying a huge rucksack which had been stuffed full with booty. A bra strap poked out through the side of the rucksack.

'And so far they all seem to be the same size.'

'Which is?'

'40DD,' replied Thumper.

'An unusually large size, apparently,' said Patchy.

'I fear there's likely to be a shortage of suitable customers,' added Thumper.

'Shouldn't the police be here?' I asked. 'Surely all this stuff belongs to someone?'

'Not on this occasion,' said Patchy. He nodded towards a man in a grey suit who was sitting on a rock. A brown leather briefcase was resting against his leg. 'He's a representative from the shipping line. He's told the police they're happy for people to take what they can carry.'

'Just take the stuff away?'

'None of it's any good to them,' said Thumper. 'No store wants to buy — or sell — bras that have been soaked in salt water for hours. The little metal catches at the back and the metal wires they use to help support the part of the bra that holds up the breasts will be marked and the material will stain.'

'So the insurers gave the go ahead for people to help themselves. Cheaper than clearing up the stuff themselves.'

'So why aren't you two collecting your fair share?' I asked.

'Once this lot hits the market you won't be able to sell a sized 40DD bra in Devon,' said Thumper.

'Not worth picking them up,' said Patchy. '80,000 bras. All the same size. It's difficult to imagine a more worthless cargo.'

They turned and headed back up the hill to where they'd parked their cars. I went with them.

'Dee Dee Protheroe will be all right for bras for a while,' said Patchy.

'Who on earth is Dee Dee Protheroe?' I asked.

'The vicar's wife,' said Thumper.

'Eileen Protheroe?'

'How many large-bosomed Protheroes do you know?'

I thought about it. 'Just Eileen, I suppose,' I admitted.

The vicar's wife's most notable feature was an enormous bosom which bounced and swayed and had a life of its own. I had once been present at a cricket match on the village green in Bilbury when Archie Grimshaw, playing for Parracombe Thirds, had hit a long hop from Peter Marshall (who doesn't usually play cricket but had been press-ganged when it was discovered that we only had ten men available) and the ball had landed in Mrs Protheroe's cleavage. She had been standing on the grass at the edge of the green at the time and it was quickly decided that she was, therefore, on the cricket field. Naturally, this meant that the ball was still in play. Several of the fielders volunteered to pick the ball out of its resting place (it had more or less disappeared from sight and only a thin segment of the ball was still visible) but after protests from both batsmen, a group of spectators and a very red-faced vicar, the umpires decreed that this wouldn't be entirely 'cricket'.

It was eventually decided that Mrs Protheroe should be allowed to remove the ball herself and to then hurl it as high into the air as she could manage. The fielders would then be allowed to try to catch it. Only if they succeeded would the batsman be given out. Mrs Protheroe managed to extract the ball and then, throwing underarm, tried to hurl it into the air. Unfortunately, her arm didn't stop soon enough and instead of going upwards the ball went backwards over her right shoulder. It ended up in the car park in front of the Duck and Puddle. The batsman, Archie Grimshaw, immediately claimed that he'd hit a six and, although it was difficult to argue with his logic, the umpires did so for another twenty five minutes before deciding that, although it was the brightest day of the summer, the light was too bad to continue and they would abandon the match as a draw.

'But why do you call her Dee Dee?' I asked. 'Her name is Eileen.'

'No one called her Eileen until she married the vicar,' said Thumper.

'She was born and brought up in Combe Martin,' said Patchy. 'She was known as Dee Dee from when she was about 16.'

'So why is she now known as Eileen?' I asked as we arrived at Thumper's truck. He opened one door and Patchy opened the other. Naturally, Thumper hadn't bothered to lock the truck.

'I don't suppose she thinks that being called by her bra size is quite proper for a vicar's wife,' said Thumper, getting into his truck.

He and Patchy waved as they drove away.

The sudden abundance of bras was a boon for large bosomed women in North Devon.

But it seemed there weren't enough gener-
ously endowed women around and the bras
rapidly became an example of the sort of glut
that can affect strawberry growers in the
middle of the season. Every pub for miles
around contained far more than its fair share
of struggling salesmen failing to offload their
stock of over-sized bras. Hope and joy quickly
turned to disappointment and despair as they
all found themselves failing to make a single
sale.

To my astonishment I heard a little later
that Thumper and Patchy had gone round the
pubs buying up all the bras which had been
salvaged but had failed to sell.

'Did you find a large supply of well-
endowed ladies?' I asked them when I next
saw them in the Duck and Puddle.

Thumper shook his head. 'We found a
melon grower in Somerset who gave us a
good price. He normally uses netting bags to
support his melons as they develop. He was
thrilled.'

I stared at him, disbelievingly.

'Melons need support,' explained Patchy.
'As the fruits ripen they get heavy, break free
of their stalks and crash to the ground.'

'So the growers have to buy special nets to
stop them falling before they're ready for
picking,' said Thumper.

'Two melons to a plant is apparently quite normal,' said Patchy. 'So bras are just perfect.'

'And DD bras are just the right size for melons?' I asked.

'A perfect fit,' said Thumper, holding out two cupped hands as though to demonstrate. 'The very best melon is apparently the same size as a DD breast.'

Thumper and Patchy have been friends of mine since I arrived in Bilbury. I am, however, constantly amazed at their imaginations and ingenuity.

'With your brains you two could do great things!' I told them.

They looked at each other and, without speaking a word, both put their hands into their back pockets and pulled out bulging wallets.

'We turned a load of unwanted bras into perfectly good drinking vouchers,' said Patchy. 'What other great thing did you have in mind?'

I couldn't think of a reply so, although they were the ones with the bulging wallets, I bought another round of drinks.

The Visitors

I was in the Duck and Puddle one lunchtime, sitting with Thumper Robinson and Patchy Fogg, when a pleasant, friendly-looking couple I'd never seen before came in. He wore brown corduroy trousers and a red sweater. She wore grey trousers and a pale pink V-necked sweater with a white blouse. They looked around and then walked up to the bar and spoke to Gilly. After listening to them for a moment Gilly pointed in our direction. The man and the woman thanked Gilly and then walked across to where we were sitting.

'You're Thumper!' said the woman. It was a statement and not a question. She looked excited, as though she were meeting a film star.

For a moment Thumper looked puzzled.

'We haven't met,' said the woman, partly in explanation and partly in apology, 'but my husband and I are keen readers of the Bilbury books. We feel as though we know you.' She paused. 'You're our favourite character,' she added quietly.

'Ah,' said Thumper, understanding. 'Well,

you mustn't believe everything you read.'

The couple laughed. 'Oh, but we do!' said the woman. 'Don't we Gerald?'

Gerald said they did. 'My favourite book is Bilbury Revels,' he said.

'Did that cricket match really happen like that?' asked the woman.

'Absolutely,' said Thumper. 'Pretty much anyway. The doc, the chap who writes the books, exaggerates a bit occasionally.'

'Usually to make himself look good,' said Patchy.

'Are you Patchy?' the woman asked me.

I shook my head and pointed to Patchy. 'He's Patchy,' I said.

'It's wonderful to meet you too,' said the woman. 'You're our second favourite character.' She spoke as though he and Thumper were characters in a book, inventions created by an author to flesh out a piece of fiction.

'Thank you,' said Patchy, graciously.

'But I'm afraid we're not in the market for any of Shakespeare's old furniture!' laughed Gerald.

'Oh no, we're not that gullible!' laughed the woman.

'Pity,' said Patchy. 'I've got Shakespeare's writing desk in my garage.'

'Really?' said Gerald.

'Don't be silly, Gerald!' said the woman. She poked him in the ribs.

We all laughed.

'Well I suppose we'd better leave you three to your lunch,' said the woman.

'We're going to look for Bilbury Grange,' said Gerald. 'Can you give us directions?'

Thumper gave them accurate directions.

Just as they left the woman turned back and spoke to me. 'Are you anyone?' she asked.

'Oh no,' I replied quickly, before either Patchy or Thumper could speak. 'I'm just passing through.'

'Are you sure?' asked Gerald. 'We know all the local people. We've read all the Bilbury books. We'll know you even if you're a minor character.'

'Positive,' I said. 'I'm not even a minor character.'

'Pity,' said Gerald.

'Still, it's nice to have met you two,' said the woman, speaking to Patchy and Thumper.

'They're just like the books aren't they?' I heard Gerald say as they left.

'Except I didn't expect Thumper to be that good looking,' said the woman. 'And he looks younger than I expected too.'

We ate in silence for a moment or two.

'You owe us both drinks,' Patchy said to me.

'Hush money,' said Thumper.

I bought them a pint of beer and a pickled egg each.

Postscript

The Doc
by
Thumper Robinson

The doc never tells readers much about himself and so the publishers of the Bilbury books have asked me to write a few sentences about him. The publishers said they wouldn't change what I wrote and they said it as though I should be pleased but that's not much of a blessing to be honest, if it's supposed to be, since before writing this the longest thing I ever wrote was my shopping list to take to the builders' yard when I was rebuilding Miss Dawson's greenhouse, and the bad news is that I forgot the putty and had to drive all the way back into Barnstaple to fetch it so don't hold out high hopes or expect anything with smart words that you have to look up in the dictionary because before I could use them I'd have to look them up and how could I look them up if I didn't know what they were in the first place? The publishers gave me a tape recorder no bigger than an alarm clock and said if I didn't want to write stuff down I could just record it and they'd print it as I said it which is probably better for everyone and so that's what I'm doing.

The doc is a tall bloke but not what I'd call big; not muscular like most of the fellows round Bilbury. You can tell straight away that he's spent his life bashing books and not chopping down trees. When I first met him I thought he was a bit weedy to be honest. He looked like he'd blow away in a gale. He's a lot bigger now, of course. Patsy has fattened him up and he's beginning to develop a paunch and I don't suppose he'd deny that himself if you were to ask him. It was quite a surprise when he and Patsy first got it together. But before long everyone agreed that they were a perfect match. Nothing wrong with a bit of a stomach on a man, of course, and that stuff about him having a bit of a paunch is not intended as a criticism because I wouldn't criticise the doc anyway because he's my friend and my dad taught me that you don't criticise your friends in private or in public. My dad didn't leave me much but that's stuck with me and I think it's good advice which I'll pass on to my little ones when they're old enough, which to be honest I think they probably are. I'm glad I'm doing this because it's reminded me and now I can mention it to them tonight or maybe at the weekend. My mum always used to say that if a man was too skinny it was evidence that his wife wasn't looking after him properly. And I've no room to talk, as I'll readily admit.

When he first arrived in Bilbury the doc had a lot of hair. Sticking out all over the place it was. My Anne said he looked as though he'd been dragged through a hedgerow backwards and then dragged back through it forwards. But it wasn't meant nasty. He doesn't have so much hair now, of course but then we don't call him 'young doc' any more. Patsy makes sure he keeps it trimmed though to be honest with you God has done quite a good job of thinning it out for him.

When the doc first came to Bilbury as assistant to Dr Brownlow we were all a bit suspicious of him to tell the truth. Maybe suspicious isn't the right word. Wary would perhaps be a better way of putting it.

But slowly he earned respect and it soon became clear that he was taken with the village. People liked that. We like things to stay the same here. I think villagers were worried that we'd get used to him and then just when we'd got used to his little ways and he'd got used to ours he'd be up and off somewhere better. There was a bit of resentment when he first arrived — though we all tried not to show it. Everyone in the village liked and trusted Dr Brownlow and selfishly we didn't want anything to change though we all knew he was getting older and couldn't go on for ever. If you know anything about Bilbury you will know that we aren't big on change — even if it is wrapped up as progress. We aren't that keen on progress either to be perfectly honest with you.

If you asked me to describe the sort of person the doc is I'd say he's a damned good bloke and the village was lucky to get him as our doctor. I know we should respect all medical men, because they've all gone through a lot of training and learning and so on, but to tell the truth there are some I've met that I wouldn't want looking after me or my Anne. The doc is a gentleman, which in my book is the biggest compliment you can pay, but nevertheless he is the sort of mate you can have a drink with and, more important, the sort of bloke you can rely on. He doesn't look down on people who haven't had his learning and he's always keen to learn about other people and their skills. I remember him being very impressed that I could tickle a trout which to be blunt with you isn't much of a trick at all when you know how to do it. We respect a man like that in Bilbury. Patchy Fogg, the antique dealer, says the doc reminds him a bit of that Don Quixote we were told about in school. It took me a while to remember who he meant because to begin with I got Don Quixote mixed up with Don Corleone who is someone else completely different of course and, as I understand it, probably not a real person at all, though since they both have the same Christian name you will see how I got confused. It's the same Christian name as that Australian cricketer Don Bradman who was someone entirely different. I never saw him play myself but they say he was good and he was a hero of mine even though he was a foreigner. Eric Hollies bowled him in his final Test Match otherwise he would have averaged over 100 in Tests. Don Quixote was a Spanish gentleman I believe. I've never known anyone called Don myself, though when the regular driver who delivers to Peter Marshall from the wholesaler was ill with a broken wrist (which I happen to know he got falling over in a bit of a drunken state one Saturday night but which he told everyone he did slipping on a wet cabbage leaf so that he wouldn't get the boot and who could blame him for that and it doesn't matter now because he's retired and gone up far north to live in Keynsham which is where that Horace Batchelor used to live, who did the pools adverts on Radio Luxembourg when I was a kid listening to the radio under my bedclothes though my Mum told me years later that she always knew anyway) his replacement stand-in for a while was a bloke called Don who had a tattoo of a mermaid on his arm and claimed he'd been in the Navy but none of us believed him because in a conversation he had with Patchy it was clear that he didn't know where the Pacific Ocean was and a sailor would know that, though we didn't say anything because there's nothing worse than embarrassing someone unnecessarily.

When the doc first started writing his books we had some worries that he would end up attracting tourists to the village and change things but to be honest things haven't been too bad. The doc says that not too many people read books these days and that unless they make a television series out of the books we don't have a thing to worry about and he says there isn't much chance of that which is, to be honest, a blessing because we don't want the place flooding with gawping tourists. We had that problem once before and the doc described it pretty well in one of his books though I forget which one (*Bilbury Country*

— *Editor*) but nevertheless although I'm not what you'd normally call a vain person (my Anne is always telling me I should take more care with my appearance, like nagging me to change a shirt when we go out to the Duck and Puddle) I wouldn't mind seeing who they'd get to play me on the screen. Personally if they're going to do something like that I'd rather it was a proper film but the doc says the chances of that are even smaller than the chances of us being a television series.

The doc says his books so far are all set in the 1970s, when he first arrived in Bilbury, but to be honest little has changed and we're living in a sort of time warp I suppose. From reading the books we have all learned a good deal about ourselves (and in particular about the way other people see us) but the gift the doc gave us is that we hadn't realised just how lucky we are to live in Bilbury. If you love somewhere wonderful you tend to take it for granted, especially if you've never known anything different as I haven't.

The doc gets letters from readers asking him if Bilbury really exists. Well, all I can say is that if it doesn't I'd like to know where I've been living all my life. He also gets letters wanting to know how real everything is. I don't know what he says to them but all I can say to that is that there are some things I don't think he gets quite right but to be truthful with you his books are pretty accurate except that Peter Marshall (*who runs the village shop — Editor*) is a darned sight meaner and Frank (*the publican who runs the Duck and Puddle — Editor*) is a damned sight drunker than the doc makes him out to be. And Frank and Gilly (*Frank's wife — Editor*) have some real ding dong fights that the doc doesn't mention, though I expect that's out of respect, and since they've been married a good long time I think it's safe to assume that they don't mean much of what they say to each other. I can't speak for the medical stuff of course, me not being a doctor or having any medical knowledge, but you can take my word for it that the village is just as he describes it. I used to think that he made me out to be a bit of a Jack the Lad, as my mother used to say, but over the years I've come round to thinking that he's probably got me just about right. Patchy Fogg once got a bit upset with the doc giving away a few of the tricks he uses at auctions but Patchy and the doc soon thought up some new ones which the doc promised not to put in any of his books, and the two of them shook hands and everything is fine again now.

Sometimes the doc strikes me as a bit of a

champion of lost causes. But as Jimmy Stewart says in Frank Capra's film *Mr Smith Goes To Washington* those are the only causes worth fighting for and I respect him for that. Anne, my other half, and I like the cinema and that's our favourite film. Jimmy Stewart and Humphrey Bogart are our favourite actors, and Frank Capra is our favourite director. A lot of people never know the names of film directors but I think it's important because although it's the stars you see on the screen, it's the director who decides what you see them doing, and if they just stood there doing nothing it would be a pretty glum sort of film.

One of the doc's medical friends came to stay once (*Bilbury Village: Editor*) and I talked to him a bit while he was here. He said the doc's problem was that he had always been 'idealistic, professionally naive and unworldly'. I remember the words well. I didn't see anything wrong with any of those things. It's true the doc is sometimes a bit of an innocent, but he's passionate and sensitive and in my mind those are things that make a good doctor. He can't stand prejudice, intolerance and hypocrisy which I don't much like either. If you're going to pick out his faults I'd say he was a bit impatient (I once took him to see the badgers playing at night and after forty minutes of waiting he was fidgeting so much that I took him back home). He can be infuriatingly touchy and a bit old-fashioned in many ways but most of us in Bilbury just ignore his touchiness which we've got used to and you can't be too old-fashioned for us. I now find it difficult to believe just how innocent the doc was when I first met him; when he first arrived in Bilbury. He had not long qualified and I don't think he had much experience of general practice. He was very much a towny too. He couldn't tell the difference between an oak and a chestnut and that caused us a few laughs at the time I don't mind telling you, though we would never laugh at a man behind his back! The doc still can't change a wheel but he knows a bit about trees and wildlife now and if he needs a wheel changing he's only got to call and there's half a dozen of us glad to do it for him.

The doc questions and challenges pomposity and he hates bureaucrats as much as I do. Actually, as much as we all do. He sticks up for the village because he can talk back to them and they have to listen to him because he's by way of being a doctor and a learned man. And he doesn't give a fig for the consequences which is something else to respect him for.

You might have imagined that the doc and I might have fallen out over his love of animals. He and Patsy are the only two vegetarians I know, and when Patsy turned and stopped eating meat her family were terribly upset. Her father thought she was going to die without meat on her plate and made quite a fuss but she stood firm and in the end he respected that. It was the same with the doc and me. He knows I catch animals to eat but we don't fall out about it. Occasionally, he tries to convert me but I just laugh at him and then we forget about it. We don't hold grudges. You have to respect the other person's point of view if you live in a small village.

Anyway, I'd much rather have the doc with his faults than that other doctor who came to visit. (*Thumper is again referring to an incident described in Bilbury Village — Editor*). That doctor struck me as being smug and a damned snob. He wouldn't fit in around Bilbury I can tell you that for free. He was a bit cynical I thought. Here in Bilbury we respect the old values such as commitment, honesty and loyalty. Judging by what I've heard and read and what I see when I go travelling to places like Barnstaple or Exeter these may not be valued much in the outside world but here in Bilbury these are things we consider important.

I hope this is the sort of thing you wanted because to be honest with you I'm really pleased to be able to say a few words about the doc, who is as good a friend as I ever had or hope to have. The doc and I aren't exactly what you might call the sort who you would expect to get on together, him being a man of learning and me being, well, not a man of any learning at all. I'll be very proud to see words of mine in a book, especially a book about Bilbury, though to be honest with you again I'll believe it when I see it because I can't believe anyone would print anything I'd write because if you want a roof mending, a car clock putting back or a pheasant plucking I'm your man but I wouldn't hire me to write a letter for you let alone something for a book.

If you want to tidy this up or make it read better I wouldn't mind a dab but just please make sure that it's clear that all of us in Bilbury like the doc very much, me and Anne especially, and we couldn't have a better doctor in the village and I would never say anything but good things about him because he's not just the doctor and a real gentleman but I'm proud to say that he's my friend. And in my eyes a man can't say more than that.

Thumper Robinson